What makes human
languages special?

Literature Link

"All Things Bright and Beautiful"
by Cecil Frances Alexander

All things bright and beautiful,
All creatures great and small,
All things wise and wonderful,
The Lord God made them all.

Each little flower that opens,
Each little bird that sings,
He made their glowing colors,
He made their tiny wings.

The purple-headed mountains,
The river running by,
The sunset, and the morning,
That brightens up the sky.

The cold wind in the winter,
The pleasant summer sun,
The ripe fruits in the garden,
He made them every one.

The tall trees in the greenwood,
The meadows where we play,
The rushes by the water,
We gather every day;—

He gave us eyes to see them,
And lips that we might tell,
How great is God Almighty,
Who has made all things well.

Quetzal

Grand Tetons

Bird of Paradise

Practice

Common Prepositions					
about	around	beside	in	on	to
above	at	by	inside	out	under
across	before	down	near	outside	until
after	behind	for	of	over	up
along	below	from	off	through	with

Circle the preposition or prepositions.

1. Grandma sent us (to) the apple orchard (behind) the barn.
2. (Under) the tree, ripe apples lay (in) the grass.
3. Many more apples hung (below) the tree.
4. We picked apples (for) one hour.
5. The baskets were filled (with) bright red apples.
6. We placed the baskets (near) the wagon (beside) the tree.
7. (In) the house Grandma made applesauce (from) the apples.
8. (After) lunch we ate the applesauce (inside) Grandma's kitchen.

Underline the object of the preposition.

9. under the heavy <u>branches</u>
10. around the apple <u>orchard</u>
11. after the hard <u>rain</u>
12. along the dirt <u>path</u>
13. outside the <u>house</u>
14. through the <u>river</u>

Decide what the underlined prepositional phrase is telling. Mark *where*, *when*, or *how*.

15. The airport is <u>near the city</u>.
    ○ where   O when   ○ how

16. <u>Before lunch</u>, we will leave the house.
    ○ where   ○ when   ○ how

17. Our family is flying <u>in the large jet</u>.
    ○ where   ○ when   ○ how

Put parentheses around the prepositional phrase or phrases.

18. (From the airport) Wesley likes watching the planes take-off.

19. He dreams (about flying) (over tall buildings) some day.

20. He would look (at the tiny people) (below the airplane.)

21. Wesley would fly (above the mountains) and (through the clouds.)

22. (After the flight) he would head (for home.)

23. He would tip his plane and wave (to his dad) (beside their house.)

Add a prepositional phrase to expand the sentence.

24. Bella found her shoe.

_____

25. After school Elias ran.

_____

Write a sentence about something that you did yesterday. Use a prepositional phrase that tells *where*, *when*, or *how*.

26. _____

_____

Write a sentence about your home. Use a prepositional phrase.

27. _____

_____

Journal

Write several sentences telling about the differences between the ways that parrots use words and the ways that people use words.

1. _____

_____

_____

_____

Write a sentence telling why you think a parrot cannot use language in the same way that humans can. Consider what makes humans different from animals based on the Creation story in Genesis.

2. _____

_____

Writing an Acrostic Poem

How is writing like making a craft?

Literature Link

"Piano" from *Bow-Tie Pasta: Acrostic Poems* by Brian P. Cleary

Parading down Main Street
Is a sea of red-uniformed players of flute
And clarinet and drum,
Navigating their way through confetti and applause.
Only wish that I could march with *my* instrument.

"Top Secret" from *BookSpeak!: Poems About Books* by Laura Purdie Salas

Describe your desires and they become mine.
I'm a treasure box where feelings can shine.
All thinkers need pages where dreams can take flight.
Reveal all
Your secrets, one entry per night.

The Craft of Writing

Cora and Cameron completed similar steps for their projects. Read the sentence that describes a step Cora completed as she made a craft. Find the step Cameron completed as he wrote a poem that best matches Cora's step.

C   1. Cora plans to knit a scarf for her grandfather.

B   2. Cora picks out blue yarn at the store.

D   3. Cora decides to knit six extra inches to make the scarf longer.

E   4. Cora takes out a row of uneven stitches and knits it again.

A   5. Cora gives the scarf to Grandpa for his birthday.

A Cameron mails the poem to his uncle in Kenya.

B Cameron chooses to spell *giraffe* with the first letters of each line.

C Cameron decides to write an acrostic poem.

D Cameron changes the word *brown* to *chocolate*.

E Cameron corrects two misspelled words in his poem.

Write the name of an art or craft project.

6. Art or craft project: _____

List what you would need to have and do in order to complete the art or craft project well.

7. What I would need:

_____

_____

_____

_____

_____

_____

_____

_____

_____

Write a sentence describing one way making this art or craft project is like writing a poem.

8. _____

_____

Learning More about Acrostic Poems

An **acrostic poem** can be read both across and down. It uses certain letters in each line to spell another word or message.

These letters are usually the first or last letters of the line.

My German shepherd
Always gets in trouble for
Jumping up
On our sofa and barking—
Ruff! Ruff!

When read vertically, these letters spell a word or phrase.

Soft breeze rustling
Up in the trees,
Mornings with no school,
Making me feel lazy,
Evenings of playing outside,
Racing the wind on my bike.

PICKing a Word for Your Acrostic

Poetic	Choose a word that would make a good **poetry** topic.
Interesting	Find an **interesting** word that you would enjoy writing about.
Careful	Be **careful** about choosing words with unusual letters, such as *X* or *Z*. You may have trouble finding words that start with these letters.
Keep looking	**Keep looking** for other words beginning with these letters that you could use to tell about your topic.

Draft lines for an acrostic poem with your partner.

S <u>chool is so fun and homework</u>
<u>is so easy.</u>

C <u>we live in a christion school.</u>
<u> </u>

H <u> </u>
<u> </u>

O <u> </u>
<u> </u>

O <u> </u>
<u> </u>

L <u> </u>
<u> </u>

Acrostic Poem: Plan

Psalm 119 was written in Hebrew as an acrostic poem. The whole psalm is about God's Word.

> The Hebrew alphabet has 22 letters.

> Each letter begins 8 lines of poetry.

> Hebrew reads from right to left.

א אַשְׁרֵי תְמִימֵי־דָרֶךְ הַהֹלְכִים בְּתוֹרַת יְהֹוָה׃ ¹

א אַשְׁרֵי נֹצְרֵי עֵדֹתָיו בְּכָל־לֵב יִדְרְשׁוּהוּ׃ ²

א אַף לֹא־פָעֲלוּ עַוְלָה בִּדְרָכָיו הָלָכוּ׃ ³

א אַתָּה צִוִּיתָה פִקֻּדֶיךָ לִשְׁמֹר מְאֹד׃ ⁴

א אַחֲלַי יִכֹּנוּ דְרָכָי לִשְׁמֹר חֻקֶּיךָ׃ ⁵

א אָז לֹא־אֵבוֹשׁ בְּהַבִּיטִי אֶל־כָּל־מִצְוֺתֶיךָ׃ ⁶

א אוֹדְךָ בְּיֹשֶׁר לֵבָב בְּלָמְדִי מִשְׁפְּטֵי צִדְקֶךָ׃ ⁷

א אֶת־חֻקֶּיךָ אֶשְׁמֹר אַל־תַּעַזְבֵנִי עַד־מְאֹד׃ ⁸

1 Blessed are the undefiled in the way, who walk in the law of the Lord.

2 Blessed are they that keep his testimonies, and that seek him with the whole heart.

3 They also do no iniquity: they walk in his ways.

4 Thou hast commanded us to keep thy precepts diligently.

5 O that my ways were directed to keep thy statutes!

6 Then shall I not be ashamed, when I have respect unto all thy commandments.

7 I will praise thee with uprightness of heart, when I shall have learned thy righteous judgments.

8 I will keep thy statutes: O forsake me not utterly.

Rudolf Kittel, *Biblia Hebraica*,
(Lipsiae, Germany: J. C. Hinrichs, 1909), 1002.

Compare Psalm 119 in Hebrew to the acrostic poem "Top Secret" by Laura Purdie Salas on Worktext page 28. Complete the chart.

Two Kinds of Acrostic Poems		
	Psalm 119	**"Top Secret"**
Topic:	Gods word	diary
Letters for acrostic:		
Number of lines:		
Language:		

Ideas for an Acrostic Poem

1. Yourself, a family member, or a pet (Adam, Grandpa, Kitty)
2. A month or a season of the year (March, winter)
3. A flower (rose, tulip)
4. Your favorite holiday (Easter, Christmas)
5. A color (purple, black)
6. Your favorite food (cupcakes, tacos)
7. An activity you like to do (swimming, baseball)

Write your acrostic word on the line. Leave space between the letters. Beneath each letter list words beginning with that letter that you could use to tell about your topic.

Acrostic word:

D C   E   C   E   M   B   E   R
decorarshin exiting cool exilet most bring remember

birthday

E

C

E

M

Acrostic Poem: Draft

The punctuation you choose will help your poem move quickly or slowly to fit your topic. Punctuation can create pauses in your poem.

Poems with very few pauses at the ends of the lines move quickly.

Poems with many pauses at the ends of lines move more slowly.

Soft breeze blowing

Up in the trees,

Mornings with no school,

Making me feel lazy,

Evnings of playing,

Riding my bike.

Drafting Guide

Write your acrostic word vertically down the page.

Check the spelling of your acrostic word.

Look at your word list for words to use in your poem.

Use punctuation to create movement (fast or slow) that goes with your topic.

Use the drafting guide to help you draft your acrostic poem.

Does you like Christmess?
Every time it is so fun,
christ was born that day, and cool
Every minute it gets closer and closer
more and more we all get presents,
Beter bring pleasents then it is beter,
Every present we get we love it,
Rooles as much as Summer

Acrostic Poem: Revise and Proofread

Nathan 1

Writers can help each other improve. In a peer conference, be sure to speak kindly, listen carefully, and ask questions. Try using these sentence starters.

"I really liked . . ."   *"Do you think . . ."*

"I had a question about . . ."   *"It might be clearer to say . . ."*

> *rustling*
> Soft breeze ~~blowing~~
>
> Up in the trees,
>
> Mornings with no school,
>
> Making me feel lazy,
>
> Evnings of playing,
> *Racing the wind on*
> ~~Riding~~ my bike.

Proofreading Marks

∧∨	Add
ℰ	Delete
≡	Capital letter
/	Lowercase
⟳→	Move

Use the revising checklist to help you revise your acrostic poem.

Revising Checklist	
✓	The acrostic word in my poem is spelled correctly.
✓	My poem tells about the acrostic word.
✓	My poem has exact and interesting words.
✓	The movement (fast or slow) of my poem goes with my topic.

Soft breeze rustling

Up in the trees,

Mornings with no school,

Making me feel lazy,

Evenings

~~Evnings~~ of playing,

Racing the wind on my bike.

Use the proofreading checklist to help you proofread your acrostic poem.

Proofreading Checklist		
My poem makes sense.		
I used correct spelling.		
Each line of my poem begins with a capital letter.		

Reflection

Jon has done sloppy work on his acrostic poem. He finished it in a hurry so he could rush outside to play. The poem is full of mistakes and boring words, and it doesn't make sense. It is not well crafted.

Answer the questions about Jon and his writing.

1. What is the best reason you can think of that Jon should try harder to write a poem that is well crafted?

   _____

   _____

2. How could Jon use language tools and skills to improve his writing next time?

   _____

   _____

Cumulative Review

Mark the group of words that is a sentence.

1. ○ Threw the ball to Coach Ward.
   ○ In the first soccer field.
   ○ Juan kicked the soccer ball.

2. ○ The croaking bullfrog in the slimy mud.
   ○ The bullfrog sounds like a cow mooing.
   ○ Croaking loudly in the summer evening.

3. ○ The helpful librarian at the public library.
   ○ Sorted the children's magazines into stacks.
   ○ She carefully arranged the books in the library.

4. ○ Grandpa slowly turned the key to start the tractor.
   ○ The putt, putt noise of the old green tractor.
   ○ Moving slowly and carefully around the hay field.

5. ○ The Statue of Liberty a gift from France to the United States.
   ○ Standing over 150 feet high in New York Harbor.
   ○ Lady Liberty is a symbol of freedom throughout the world.

Mark the sentence with the correct end punctuation.

6. ○ Last night, Father took Mother on a date?
   ○ My father thinks my mother is beautiful.
   ○ What does the Bible say about a husband loving his wife!

7. ○ What is your favorite cookie?
   ○ My grandmother bought flour on Saturday!
   ○ Oh, how delicious is a warm, gooey chocolate cookie.

8. ○ Did you arrive at the boarding gate on time.
   ○ Hurray, we made it!
   ○ Soon the huge jet will taxi down the runway?

9. ○ My sister gathers eggs from the nesting box!
   ○ Are the blue eggs from an Araucana hen.
   ○ What color eggs do your hens lay?

10. ○ Doctors stick your arm and look in your nose?
    ○ Does your doctor give you yucky tasting medicine.
    ○ The doctor saved my sister's life!

Choose the best way to combine the sentences.

11. God made the animals on the earth. God created man in His image.
    - ○ God made the animals on the earth and God created man in His image.
    - ○ God made the animals on the earth, God created man in His image.
    - ○ God made the animals on the earth, but God created man in His image.

12. Eve trusted the words of a snake. Eve doubted the words of God.
    - ○ Eve trusted the words of a snake and, Eve doubted the words of God.
    - ○ Eve trusted the words of a snake, but she doubted the words of God.
    - ○ Eve trusted the words of a snake, Eve doubted the words of God.

13. Eve ate the fruit. Eve gave the fruit to Adam.
    - ○ Eve ate the fruit and gave the fruit to Adam.
    - ○ Eve ate the fruit Eve gave the fruit to Adam.
    - ○ Eve ate the fruit but Eve gave the fruit to Adam.

14. Adam heard God's command. Adam chose to disobey God.
    - ○ Adam heard God's command but Adam chose to disobey God.
    - ○ Adam heard God's command, but he chose to disobey God.
    - ○ Adam heard God's command, he chose to disobey God.

15. Adam had to leave the beautiful garden. Eve had to leave the beautiful garden.
    - ○ Adam had to leave the beautiful garden and Eve had to leave the beautiful garden.
    - ○ Adam had to leave the beautiful garden Eve had to leave the beautiful garden.
    - ○ Adam and Eve had to leave the beautiful garden.

Choose the best preposition to complete the sentence.

16. Max sleeps _____ his doghouse.
    - ○ with   ○ in   ○ at

17. Max chased the tabby cat _____ the big oak tree.
    - ○ around   ○ on   ○ above

18. Our dog Max hides _____ the couch when he is naughty.
    - ○ above   ○ after   ○ behind

Nouns

What can the sky tell us?

Literature Link

Excerpt from "What Is the Hubble Space Telescope?" (NASA)

What Is the Hubble Space Telescope?

The Hubble Space Telescope is a large telescope in space. NASA launched Hubble in 1990. Hubble is as long as a large school bus. It weighs as much as two adult elephants. Hubble travels around Earth at about 5 miles per second. That is as fast as driving a car from the East Coast of the United States to the West Coast in 10 minutes.

Hubble faces toward space. It takes pictures of planets, stars and galaxies. [. . .]

What Makes Hubble Different from Telescopes on Earth?

The mixture of gases that surround a planet is called its atmosphere. Earth's atmosphere changes and blocks some of the light that comes from space. Hubble flies around, or orbits, high above Earth and its atmosphere. So, Hubble can see space better than telescopes on Earth can. Hubble is not the kind of telescope that you look through with your eye. Hubble uses a digital camera. It takes pictures like a cell phone. Then Hubble uses radio waves to send the pictures through the air back to Earth.

Confusing Proper Nouns

Some words can be **common nouns** or **proper nouns**. Common nouns that show family relationships become proper nouns when they are used as a name or part of a name.

> *My aunt brought my grandmother for a visit.*
>
> *Aunt Susan brought Grandmother for a visit.*

Common nouns that describe a geographic feature become proper nouns when they are used as a name or part of a name.

> *The mountains are not near the ocean.*
>
> *The Rocky Mountains are not near the Atlantic Ocean.*

Compass words become proper nouns when they are used to refer to a region.

> *I live north of the old church.*
>
> *There are many large cities in the North.*

Mark the sentence that is written correctly.

1. ○ "Is supper ready, mom?"
   ◉ "Is supper ready, Mom?"

2. ◉ My cousin is in the third grade.
   ○ My Cousin is in the third grade.

3. ○ Nebraska is located in the great plains region of the United States.
   ◉ Nebraska is located in the Great Plains region of the United States.

4. ○ Rice is often grown in the lowlands, a region in South Carolina.
   ◉ Rice is often grown in the Lowlands, a region in South Carolina.

Write one sentence with *grandfather* used as a common noun and another sentence with *Grandfather* used as a proper noun.

5. Common: _My grandfather is rushin._

6. Proper: _Grandfather Adom is so good at rushin_

7. ● Uncle Dan visited Cousin Jim in Washington, D.C.
   ○ Uncle Dan visited cousin Jim in Washington, D.C.

8. ○ The National Air and Space Museum is just a few miles to the North.
   ● The National Air and Space Museum is just a few miles to the north.

9. ○ My Uncle lives to the South of Cousin Jim's house.
   ● My uncle lives to the south of Cousin Jim's house.

10. ● The Pima Air & Space Museum is in the West.
    ○ The Pima Air & Space Museum is in the west.

11. ● Do you know of any space museums near Monument Valley?
    ○ Do you know of any space museums near Monument valley?

12. ○ The Space coast is an area in Florida that is famous for space museums.
    ● The Space Coast is an area in Florida that is famous for space museums.

13. ● There are several space museums in the South.
    ○ There are several space museums in the south.

Use proofreading marks to correct the six mistakes in the paragraph.

14. When my Aunt came back from her vacation in the Scottish

    highlands, she brought gifts for us. She had a scarf for my

    Grandma, a pair of gloves for Uncle Richard, and a necklace

    for me. For mom and dad, she had a painting of the coast of

    Scotland. We thanked aunt Hannah for the gifts.

Proofreading Marks

≡ Capital letter

/ Lowercase

Practice

1. What is one of your three _____?
   wish

2. I would like to take a _____ to be an astronaut.
   class

3. Many _____ send astronauts to space.
   country

4. Flying in a NASA _____ would be amazing.
   spacecraft

5. Another wish I have is to fly to other _____.
   galaxy

6. I would also like to see the mountains and _____ on the moon.
   valley

7. Someday I will be an astronaut and eat my meals from _____.
   pouch

8. For now I am content gazing at the stars and feeling the sun's _____.
   ray

9. Space travel has changed many people's _____.
   life

Rewrite the phrase using a singular possessive noun.

10. The moon belonging to Earth _____

11. The footprint belonging to Neil Armstrong _____

12. The orbit of John Glenn _____

13. The crew of the space shuttle _____

14. The space helmet worn by Cassidy _____

Rewrite the phrase using a plural possessive noun.

15. The books belonging to the children _____

16. The colors of the leaves _____

17. The goslings belonging to the geese _____

18. The coats belonging to the women _____

19. The stripes that the fish have _____

20. The tails on the puppies _____

Mark the sentence that is written correctly.

21. ○ Our family is traveling South for a family reunion.
    ○ Our family is traveling south for a family reunion.

22. ○ The Hancock family reunion will be held at Uncle David's house.
    ○ The Hancock family reunion will be held at uncle David's house.

23. ○ My uncle's house is nestled in the mountains of Virginia.
    ○ My uncle's house is nestled in the Mountains of Virginia.

24. ○ All of my cousins will be there including cousin Luke.
    ○ All of my cousins will be there including Cousin Luke.

25. ○ The aunts, uncles, and cousins will hike salt pond mountain.
    ○ The aunts, uncles, and cousins will hike Salt Pond Mountain.

Write one sentence with *mother* used as a common noun and another sentence with *Mother* used as a proper noun.

26. Common: _____

_____

27. Proper: _____

_____

Chapter 3 Review

-4½ = 90%

Underline the three nouns.

1. A group of stars is called a galaxy.
2. My friend got a telescope for Christmas.
3. These beautiful stars reflect the glory of God.

Use ≡ to mark the letters that should be capitalized.

4. mrs. hernandez teaches spanish at my school.
5. On sunday our pastor spoke about the holy spirit.
6. We made valentine's day cards for the patients at brookside hospital.

Write the correct abbreviations.

7. Wednesday _____Wed._____

8. March _____Mar._____

9. President _____pres._____

10. Reverend _____Rev._____

11. Avenue _____Ave._____

12. Road _____Rd._____

Use proofreading marks to correct the mistake in the date or address.

13. 41 Blackberry Ln.
    Adamsville, TN 38310

14. Sept. 24, 2022

Proofreading Marks	
∧∨	Add
≡	Capital letter

Rewrite the phrase using a singular possessive noun.

15. The wheel of the wagon _____wagon's wheel_____

16. The bird belonging to Rachel _____Rachel's bird_____

Rewrite the phrase using a plural possessive noun.

17. The jackets that the children have _____children's jacket_____

18. The eyes of the mice _____mice's eyes_____

19. The paws belonging to the bears _____bears' paws_____

Write the singular or plural form of the word to complete the sentence.

20. Deer are my favorite animal, but Alex prefers ___monkeys___.

monkey

21. The ___moose___ is the largest animal in the deer family.

moose

22. Deer have many predators, including ___wolves___ and coyotes.

wolf

23. ___Mice___ and deer can both live in the forest.

Mouse

24. Deer have small hooves for ___feet___.

foot

25. Chinese water deer do not have ___antlers___.

antler

Mark the sentence that is written correctly.

26. ● Can you tell me which direction is North?

○ Can you tell me which direction is north?

27. ● The Appalachian Mountains reach as far as Alabama.

○ The Appalachian mountains reach as far as Alabama.

28. ● We picked berries near Lake Lanier.

○ We picked berries near Lake lanier.

29. ○ Next summer we will go to the Ocean.

● Next summer we will go to the ocean.

Write one sentence with *aunt* used as a common noun and another sentence with *Aunt* used as a proper noun.

30. Common: ___My aunt is a very good cooker___

31. Proper: ___Aunt stacy is a good cook.___

Imagine that these stars can talk. Write down what they might say.

_____

_____

_____

_____

_____

_____

_____

_____

_____

Cumulative Review

Mark the sentence that is written correctly.

1. ○ Created the heaven and the earth.
   ○ And the evening and the morning.
   ○ God created man to rule over the earth.

2. ○ In the cool of the day, the voice of God.
   ○ God talked to Adam in the cool of the day.
   ○ Walking in the garden in the cool of the day.

3. ○ God the Father, Son, and Holy Spirit speak to each other.
   ○ Speaking in psalms, hymns, and spiritual songs.
   ○ O Lord, my strength and my redeemer.

4. ○ The brilliant stars, shining moons, and glowing planets.
   ○ The glory of God to all people in the whole earth.
   ○ The heavens show the glory of God.

5. ○ Pluto is a dwarf planet it is smaller than other planets.
   ○ Pluto spins in the opposite direction of Earth.
   ○ Orbits the sun as the large planets.

6. ○ Mercury the closest planet to the sun.
   ○ Mercury is the smallest planet it does not have a moon.
   ○ Sometimes, Mercury can be seen in the sky after sunset.

7. ○ Mountains, valleys, canyons, flat plains, and volcanoes.
   ○ Earth has water, but no water can be found on Venus.
   ○ Venus is smaller than Earth but, it has no moon.

8. ○ Space probes and unmanned spacecraft.
   ○ Gather information and send pictures to Earth.
   ○ The pictures show landforms, and the landforms are like those on Earth.

9. ○ God created the earth He made the sun, moon, and stars.
   ○ The sun the closest star to Earth.
   ○ God created the sun, and God created the moon.

Mark the sentence with the correct end punctuation.

10. ○ How many books are in the Bible!
    ○ How does God speak to people today?
    ○ Is the Bible the inspired Word of God.

11. ○ God created language?
    ○ Is God holy.
    ○ We have an awesome God!

12. ○ The Bible is God's special Word to man.
    ○ The earth shows the work of God?
    ○ Are your words pleasing to God!

13. ○ Should I love my neighbor.
    ○ Who is my neighbor?
    ○ God made us to love others!

14. ○ Can an animal speak like a man!
    ○ My parrot can talk?
    ○ God spoke and created all things.

Mark the sentence with a prepositional phrase underlined.

15. ○ In the beginning God created the heaven and the earth.
    ○ The world was created in six days.
    ○ The Bible is the most reliable source of truth.

16. ○ A star is a ball of gas.
    ○ At night you may see many dots of light.
    ○ Most of the dots of light are stars.

17. ○ Since Bible times people have studied the stars.
    ○ Scientists who study the stars are called astronomers.
    ○ Galileo used a telescope to look at the night sky.

18. ○ An astronaut travels and works in space.
    ○ Astronauts in space take pictures of the earth.
    ○ Some astronauts have walked on the moon.

Writing a Book Review

How could my good reasons help someone?

Literature Link

Excerpt from *Silent Road to Rescue* by Denise Williamson

Kwei Er's eyes widened. "Mu Shi, is this day really Sunday?"

"Yes, it is."

"Then you are running *and* working on Sunday!"

Mu Shi looked at him and then at Uncle. "Jesus Christ is Lord of the Sabbath. It is not the Sabbath that I wish to honor with my life. It is the Lord of the Sabbath."

Mu Shi's eyes moved to Xin Shen who painfully changed position on his narrow wooden seat. Though the great, dark bandages kept his head from turning, the man glanced around fearfully.

Mu Shi went to comfort him. "Can you stand for a moment against me to stretch your legs?" the pastor asked.

"No!" Xin Shen mumbled. "We must go on."

"We can see in all directions here," Mu Shi assured him as Uncle checked the man in the cart. "No one is near us. That is why we rest now."

The man struggled to look at the sky. "It was safer . . . when it snowed. Bad weather keeps away bandits. It slows soldiers down."

Mu Shi nodded. "I have lived in China long enough to know these things. But I also know that God watches over even the things we cannot see. Please, do not worry. I believe God is directing us."

"What is this day you call . . . Sabbath?" Xin Shen asked as Uncle returned to them.

Mu Shi seemed to wait for Uncle to speak, but when he did not, Mu Shi explained. "God made the entire world and everything in it in six days. Then on the seventh day, God rested. When God wrote the ten Great Commandments, He included the instruction that people and their beasts of burden should work for six days only and then rest on the seventh day."

"Your God makes this rule . . . yet you dare to disobey it?" Xin Shen's weary eyes filled with worry. "Then we expect misfortune . . . not divine protection now!"

Mu Shi shook his head. "No, my God is not like that," he said with confidence. "The greatest law of the Lord we serve is the law of love. 'Do well on the Sabbath days.' This also is recorded in the sacred Scriptures."

Communicating Truth

Mark the best answer.

1. What was Mu Shi's opinion in *Silent Road to Rescue*?
   - ○ God would punish Mu Shi for running or working on Sunday.
   - ○ Mu Shi could honor Jesus Christ on Sunday by helping to rescue the injured men.
   - ○ Christians should never run.

Mu Shi spoke truth to Kwei Er and Xin Shen. Read each Bible passage. Write the letter of the Bible passage next to the statement it supports.

_____ 2. "God made the entire world and everything in it in six days. Then on the seventh day, God rested. When God wrote the ten Great Commandments, He included the instruction that people and their beasts of burden should work for six days only and then rest on the seventh day."

> **A** Mark 2:27–28
> **B** Exodus 20:8–11

_____ 3. "Jesus Christ is Lord of the Sabbath. It is not the Sabbath that I wish to honor with my life. It is the Lord of the Sabbath."

Look up the Bible passage with a partner. Read the Literature Link on Worktext page 74. Write the biblical reason Mu Shi gave for making the rescue on Sunday.

4. Matthew 22:36–40

Reason: _____

_____

5. Matthew 12:10–13

Reason: _____

_____

Write a sentence telling why Mu Shi's reasons showed truth to Kwei Er and Xin Shen.

6. _____

_____

Persuading

Nathan

Persuasive writing convinces the audience to do something or to agree with the writer's opinion.

The writer supports his opinion with reasons.

I think we should all wear blue and red on the day of our spelling bee for several reasons. First, everyone would know what school we are from. We will be competing against other Christian schools in our area. Wearing our school colors would show the other students that we are from Martyn Academy. Second, we would be able to find each other easily when we all meet for lunch. But the best reason of all is that wearing blue and red would remind us to do our best. We should do our best for our school, but also for Jesus.

Opinion: I think we should wear blue and red to the spelling bee.

Reason: Everyone would know we are from Martyn Academy.

Reason: We would be able to find each other easily for lunch.

Reason: It would remind us to do our best for our school and for Jesus.

Mark the stronger reason for the opinion.

1. I think we should have class outside today.
   - ● We could learn all about clouds, flowers, and trees.
   - ○ It is a nice day.

2. Everyone in my family should come to the play.
   - ○ It would be neat.
   - ● They would all enjoy the funny plot.

3. It is important for children to take music lessons.
   - ○ They might become famous.
   - ○ They will develop skills that they can use to serve God.

4. Everyone should read a new book each month.
   - ○ Books can teach us many things.
   - ○ Books are fun to read when we don't want to do our homework.

5. I think we should take a field trip to a dairy farm.
   - ○ I want to ride the bus with my friends.
   - ○ We could learn how we get our dairy products.

6. We should have more computers at our school.
   - ○ They would look neat in our classroom.
   - ○ More students could work on school projects at the same time.

7. Everyone should learn to play basketball.
   - ○ Basketball is a fun way to get good exercise.
   - ○ Basketball is the best sport.

Write two strong reasons for the opinion.

8. I think we should give some money to a missionary this Christmas.

   Reason 1: _____

   _____

   Reason 2: _____

   _____

9. Every family should have a pet.

   Reason 1: _____

   _____

   Reason 2: _____

   _____

Parts of a Book Review

The writer of a **book review** tries to persuade the audience to feel the same way he feels about a book.

In the introduction, the writer gives the title and author of the book and states his opinion about the book.

The writer gives reasons for his opinion and supports them with examples from the book.

In the conclusion, the writer gives a recommendation about whether the audience should read the book.

Silent Road to Rescue

Do you want to read a book about danger, risk, and courage? Then I think *Silent Road to Rescue* by Denise Williamson is a terrific book for you.

First, the story is very exciting. Kwei Er and his uncle face many dangers as they travel in China in wartime to rescue two injured men. For example, Japanese soldiers try to steal their mule. A gatekeeper also refuses to let them into his city. The missionary Mu Shi even risks capture to protect them. Will Kwei Er, his uncle, and Mu Shi bring the men safely to the mission hospital? Read the book to find out.

Second, this book will teach you important lessons. Kwei Er finds out that trusting God's Word gives courage. In addition, he sees Mu Shi show God's love by giving up his coat. Mu Shi and Kwei Er's uncle choose to serve others when it could cost their lives. Reading this book taught me to be thankful that I can read the Bible.

I recommend this book to anyone who likes adventure. You won't have any trouble getting into the story, but you might have trouble putting it down!

Underline the parts of the book review. Use the colors green, blue, orange, and red.

Book Review

Introduction
Reasons
Examples
Conclusion

Opinion words **can help you state your opinion.**
Transition words **connect your ideas.**

Opinion Words	Transition Words	
I learned	first	also
I think	second	for example
I believe	third	another
my favorite	next	in addition
I like	last	for these reasons
in my opinion	finally	for instance
the best	because	in order to
	then	

Circle the opinion and transition words in the book review excerpt.

Do you want to read a book about danger, risk, and courage? Then I think *Silent Road to Rescue* by Denise Williamson is a terrific book for you.

First, the story is very exciting. Kwei Er and his uncle face many dangers as they travel in China in wartime to rescue two injured men. For example, Japanese soldiers try to steal their mule. A gatekeeper also refuses to let them into his city. The missionary Mu Shi even risks capture to protect them. Will Kwei Er, his uncle, and Mu Shi bring the men safely to the mission hospital? Read the book to find out.

Second, this book will teach you important lessons. Kwei Er learned that trusting God's Word gives courage. In addition, he sees Mu Shi show God's love by giving up his coat. Mu Shi and Kwei Er's uncle choose to serve others when it could cost their lives. Reading this book taught me to be thankful that I can read the Bible.

Plan a Book Review Together

● Work with your teacher to complete the opinion chart for a review of a book that you read together.

Title of the book: _____

Author of the book: _____

My Opinion of the Book

_____

_____

Reason 1	**Reason 2**
_____	_____
_____	_____
_____	_____
Examples from the Book	**Examples from the Book**
_____	_____
_____	_____
_____	_____
_____	_____
_____	_____

My Recommendation

_____

_____

Evaluate a Book

Think about the book you chose for your book review. Check off the questions that help you evaluate your book. List specific reasons that support your opinion about the book.

Characters

- ☑ Do they seem like real people?
- ☑ Is there one who seems a lot like you?
- ☑ Is there one who does something heroic?
- ☐ Is there one who makes a good decision?
- ☑ Did you feel sorry for any of the characters?

Setting

- ☑ Did you like the time period of the book?
- ☑ Did the place where the events happened interest you?
- ☑ When you read the book, did you feel as if you were there, in that place and time?

Plot

- ☑ Does the plot have some exciting parts?
- ☑ Does the plot have some funny parts?
- ☐ Does the plot have some sad parts?
- ☑ Does the plot have some happy parts?
- ☑ Have you ever had a problem like the one in the story?
- ☐ Do you think the characters solve their problem in a good way?

Lessons

- ☐ Did the book teach you anything new about God?
- ☐ Did the book teach you anything new about yourself?
- ☐ Did the book remind you of an important truth from God's Word?
- ☐ Did the book bring to mind something you could do to please God?
- ☑ Does the book make something bad look good?

Book title: DUCK TALES The hunt for the giant pearl

My opinion about the book: I e think this book is intrusting

Reasons for my opinion about the book: It has a intresting title. It is a good book for you and is about a pearl nd duckes

Book Review: Plan

Plan your book review using the opinion chart.

| Choose two strong reasons to support your opinion.

| List examples from the book for each reason. Your examples are the facts and details that will support your reasons.

Title of the book: _Silent Road to Rescue_

Author of the book: _Denise Williamson_

My Opinion of the Book
My new favorite book

Reason 1	Reason 2
It was exciting	_It taught important lessons_
Examples from the Book	**Examples from the Book**
Kwei Er and his uncle, dangerous trip in wartime to resque two injured men _Japanese soldiers take mule_ _Chickens make the mule act crazy_ _Gatekeeper won't let them in_ _Mu Shi risks being captured_ _Trying to reach mission hospital_	_Kwei Er—courage from God's Word_ _People very poor, thankful I have plenty to eat_ _Mu Shi loves God, unselfish_ _Mu Shi covers Kwei Er with his own coat_ _Uncle can't read, thankful I can read_ _Uncle decides to learn to read_

My Recommendation
Read if you like adventure

Use the opinion chart to plan a review of the book you chose. Choose two strong reasons and give specific examples from the book.

Title of the book: Duck Tales the hunt for the Giant Pearl

Author of the book: Disney⁺ t

My Opinion of the Book

You will ~~en~~ enjoy the Disney book.

Reason 1

I think that Glomgold is evil ting

Reason 2

I think that the babies are conpaning the day

Examples from the Book

He is trying to take the biggest pearl from the ducks He is fallowing Flintheart ducks. pearl

Examples from the Book

They are helping his dad at the cave. They are stoping Flintheart. And the pearl?

My Recommendation

you will be intrusted of the book.

Book Review: Draft

Draft your book review using the ideas from your opinion chart.

> ## Silent Road to Rescue
>
> Do you want to read a book about danger, risk, and courage. Then I think Silent Road to Rescue by Denise Williamson is a good book for you.
>
> First, the story is very exciting. Kwei Er and his Uncle face many dangers as they travel in china to resque two injured men. Japanese soldiers try to take their mule. A gatekeeper refuses to let them into his city. Will Kwei Er, his uncle, and Mu Shi bring the men to the mission hospital? Read the book to find out.

The first paragraph tells the title and author of the book.

A transition word points out the first reason.

A question raises interest in the book.

The writer states his opinion in the introduction.

The reader will have to read the book to find out what happens.

© BJU Press. Reproduction prohibited.

Opinion Words	Transition Words	
I learned	first	also
I think	second	for example
I believe	third	another
my favorite	next	in addition
I like	last	for these reasons
in my opinion	finally	for instance
the best	because	in order to
	then	

Use the ideas from your opinion chart to draft your book review. Use the drafting guide to check off the parts of a book review as you write.

Drafting Guide	
Introduction	State your opinion. Include the name of the book and its author.
Reason 1	Write a strong reason.
Examples	Give supporting examples from the book.
Reason 2	Begin your third paragraph with a strong reason.
Examples	Give supporting examples from the book.
Conclusion	Would you recommend the book to the reader?

Book Review: Revise

Revise your book review. The revising checklist can help you make improvements.

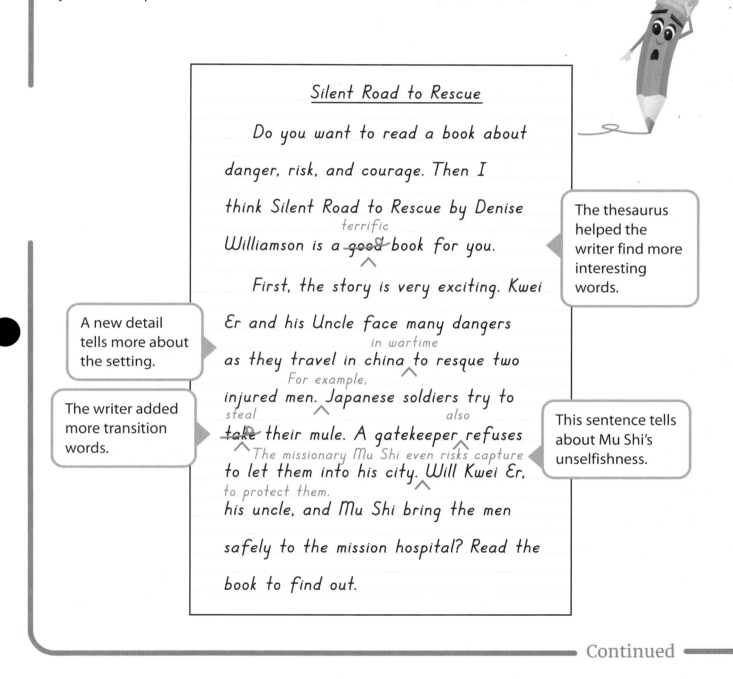

Silent Road to Rescue

Do you want to read a book about danger, risk, and courage. Then I think Silent Road to Rescue by Denise Williamson is a ~~good~~ terrific book for you.

First, the story is very exciting. Kwei Er and his Uncle face many dangers as they travel in china to resque two injured men. *in wartime* Japanese soldiers try to ~~take~~ steal their mule. *For example,* A gatekeeper refuses to let them into his city. *also* The missionary Mu Shi even risks capture Will Kwei Er, his uncle, and Mu Shi bring the men *to protect them.* safely to the mission hospital? Read the book to find out.

The thesaurus helped the writer find more interesting words.

A new detail tells more about the setting.

The writer added more transition words.

This sentence tells about Mu Shi's unselfishness.

Continued

Second, this book will teach you important lessons. Kwei Er finds out that trusting God's Word gives courage. In addition, he sees Mu Shi show God's love by giving up his coat. ~~I wish I could run fast like Mu Shi.~~ Mu Shi and Kwei Ers uncle choose to serve others when it could cost their lives. Reading this book taught me to be thankful that I can read the Bible.

> This sentence does not tell about the lessons in the book.

I recommend this book to anyone who likes adventure. You won't have any truble getting into the story you might have truble putting it down!

Proofreading Marks

∧∨	Add
ℯ	Delete
≡	Capital letter
/	Lowercase
↷→	Move

Use the revising checklist to help you revise your book review.

Revising Checklist	
My book review begins in an interesting way.	
My first paragraph includes the title and author of the book.	
I stated my opinion in the first paragraph.	
I gave two strong reasons for my opinion.	
I supported each reason with examples from the book.	
I included details about the characters, setting, and plot.	
I used interesting words and included transition words.	
My conclusion gives a recommendation to the reader.	

Book Review: Proofread

Proofread your book review to find and correct mistakes.

<u>Silent Road to Rescue</u>

Do you want to read a book about danger, risk, and courage? Then I think <u>Silent Road to Rescue</u> by Denise Williamson is a terrific book for you.

First, the story is very exciting. Kwei Er and his Uncle face many dangers as they travel in china in wartime to rescue two injured men. For example, Japanese soldiers try to steal their mule. A gatekeeper also refuses to let them into his city. The missionary Mu Shi even risks capture to protect them. Will Kwei Er, his uncle, and Mu Shi bring the men safely to the mission hospital? Read the book to find out.

Continued

Second, this book will teach you important lessons. Kwei Er finds out that trusting God's Word gives courage. In addition, he sees Mu Shi show God's love by giving up his coat. Mu Shi and Kwei Er's uncle choose to serve others when it could cost their lives. Reading this book taught me to be thankful that I can read the Bible.

I recommend this book to anyone who likes adventure. You won't have any ~~truble~~ *trouble* getting into the story *but* you might have ~~truble~~ *trouble* putting it down!

Use the proofreading checklist to help you proofread your book review.

Proofreading Checklist
I indented the first line of each paragraph.
I used complete sentences.
I began each sentence with a capital letter.
I ended each sentence with a punctuation mark.
I used correct punctuation within sentences.
I wrote proper nouns correctly.
I corrected misspelled words.

Proofreading Marks

∧∨ Add
⟋○ Delete
≡ Capital letter
∕ Lowercase
○→ Move

Speaking: Sharing Your Book Review

Good speaking is a skill that takes practice. Feeling a little nervous before speaking is normal and can actually help you speak better. You may have more energy and be more alert while you speak. Here are some things to do if you feel nervous.

Before You Speak	**While You Speak**
Pray and ask God for help.	Smile at the audience.
Take deep, quiet breaths.	Use movement.
Do exercises to help you relax.	Speak a little louder.

Continued

Tips for Good Speaking

Prepare well.	Plan ahead what you will say and how you will say it. Good preparation will help you stay calm and speak better.
Use expression.	Use your voice, face, hands, and body movements to capture and hold the interest of your audience.
Look at your audience.	Do not stare at one person, but try to look each person in the eye at least once or twice while you speak.
Speak clearly.	Enunciate your words clearly so that everyone can understand you.
Speak at a good volume.	You do not need to shout, but make sure that you speak loudly enough for everyone to hear.
Speak at a good pace.	Do not speak too slowly, and do not rush to get through.
Speak confidently.	Trust God to help you. You have prepared something important to share, and your listeners will appreciate it.

Present your book review to an audience. When you finish, mark the checklist for each thing you remembered to do while speaking.

My Speaking Self-Check

I used expression with my voice, face, hands, or body movements.	
I looked at each person in my audience while I spoke.	
I spoke clearly.	
I spoke at a good volume.	
I spoke at a good pace.	
I spoke confidently.	

Reflection

In this excerpt from Kim's book review, she follows the teacher's instructions for crafting her review. She gives a reason she liked the book. She also uses examples from the book to support her reason, and she gives a recommendation at the end.

In addition, I like this book because the main character is clever and witty. When Annie's mom asks her why she is home late from school, her story sounds so true that her mom believes her. The funny excuse she gives her teacher for late homework makes her whole class laugh. Adults can't ever prove she is lying. Reading this book showed me that some people are smart enough to get away with anything.

If you like to laugh, you will love this book. You may even collect ideas from Annie to use for yourself!

Answer the question about Kim's book review.

Will Kim's book review help her audience see the world in a truthful way? Explain why or why not.

_____

_____

_____

Cumulative Review

Mark the line with the capitalization or punctuation error.

1. ○ Our family visited the monuments in Washington, D.C.
   ○ My favorite monument is the Lincoln memorial.
   ○ It is gigantic!
   ○ The statue honors President Abraham Lincoln.

2. ○ God created man in His image.
   ○ He made man to think and to make choices.
   ○ Man uses language to tell others his thoughts.
   ○ Man can talk to god his Creator.

3. ○ God created Adam to be a man.
   ○ God created Eve to be a woman.
   ○ He created them male and female.
   ○ God created adam from the dust of the ground.

4. ○ I sat by a woman that could not read.
   ○ I shared the hymnbook with her anyway.
   ○ She listened to Pastor read the bible.
   ○ Reading is important for Sunday worship.

5. ○ My birthday is coming soon.
   ○ Mother is planning a birthday party.
   ○ We invited my friends to play at the Happy Holiday House.
   ○ The party will be on June 5 2024.

6. ○ The goose has been sitting on her eggs for thirty days.
   ○ The goslings will soon be hatching from their eggs.
   ○ The canada goose's eggs are large and creamy white.
   ○ Did you see the goose?

7. ○ My class is reading the book Misty of chincoteague.
   ○ Marguerite Henry wrote the book about a pony named Misty.
   ○ My favorite chapter is "Pony Penning Day."
   ○ What is your favorite chapter?

8. ○ Mr. Seth Dean
   ○ 125 Cherry St
   ○ Christiansburg, VA 23188
   ○ No error

Mark the sentence with a prepositional phrase underlined.

9. ○ The United States Constitution is <u>an important document</u>.
   ○ The Constitution ensures freedom <u>for all Americans</u>.
   ○ The Constitution established a <u>strong national government</u>.

10. ○ Do Americans have <u>religious freedom</u>?
    ○ The Bill of Rights <u>protects our freedom</u>.
    ○ Religious freedom is guaranteed <u>in the First Amendment</u>.

11. ○ Is an <u>amendment part</u> of the Constitution?
    ○ The <u>first ten</u> amendments are the Bill of Rights.
    ○ The Bill of Rights was written <u>after the Constitution</u>.

12. ○ Our Constitution has <u>lasted longer than</u> any other written constitution.
    ○ The writers <u>of the Constitution</u> knew the Bible well.
    ○ Christian people helped <u>make the nation</u> secure and strong.

13. ○ Government should provide justice <u>for all people</u>.
    ○ Government helps <u>people act rightly</u>.
    ○ A government must <u>punish bad behavior</u>.

Use the thesaurus entry to choose a more exact word.

bad   *adjective*
not as it should be; of poor quality
His spelling is bad.
awful, dreadful, horrible, horrid, hurtful, rotten, terrible
antonym: good

14. The bruised apple looks <u>bad</u>.
    ○ hurtful   ○ rotten   ○ dreadful

15. The children's <u>bad</u> words made the new girl feel sad.
    ○ hurtful   ○ rotten   ○ dreadful

16. Mr. Smith told the <u>bad</u> news of the car accident.
    ○ hurtful   ○ rotten   ○ dreadful

Verbs

How does a good sentence happen?

Literature Link

Excerpt from *Redwoods* by Jason Chin

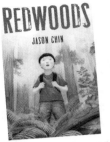

Coast redwoods need a lot of water to grow as tall as they do, and the area in Northern California where they live is perfect—it's a rain forest. The air is cool and damp, and the land is often covered in thick fog. It takes a long time for water to travel all the way from the roots to the top of a redwood, and the fog helps the trees by preventing them from losing moisture to evaporation. In addition, the needles of a redwood can absorb moisture straight from the air.

In the summer, when there is much less rainfall, redwoods have an ingenious way of collecting water: They make their own rain! When the fog rolls in, it condenses on the redwood's needles, and whatever moisture isn't absorbed then falls to the ground to be soaked up by the tree's roots. Other plants that live at the base of a redwood tree use this "artificial rain" as well, so not only do the redwoods water themselves, they water all the plants around them.

Practice

Underline the simple subject once. Underline the correct helping verb twice.

1. The soccer team (have, has) <u>won</u> six games.

2. The girls (am, are) <u>practicing</u> every day for the tournament.

3. They (do, does) <u>know</u> that the game will be tough.

4. The team (was were) <u>running</u> around the field.

5. The coach (are, is) <u>proud</u> of the girls.

6. I (does, do) <u>want</u> our team to win.

7. We (has, have) <u>worked</u> hard for a victory.

Underline the correct verb form twice.

8. My teacher (tell, told) us to respect the American flag.

9. Our class (bring, brought) the American flag to the parade.

10. The students (say, says) the Pledge of Allegiance.

11. People (thrown, threw) confetti into the air.

12. Now we (see, seen) many cheering people in the streets.

Write the correct verb form to complete the sentence.

13. Today we will _____ a ride on the old mare.
      take

14. I have _____ Molly many times.
      ride

15. Many years ago, we _____ swiftly down a trail.
      go

16. No one has _____ off her back.
      fall

17. Old Molly _____ quickly to the barn.
      run

18. Early this morning she _____ her hay in her stall.
      eat

Progressive Verbs			
Present:	am, is, are	+ *-ing* verb	is eating
Past:	was, were	+ *-ing* verb	was eating
Future:	will be	+ *-ing* verb	will be eating

> Remember that a progressive verb shows continuing action.

Underline the simple subject once and the progressive verb twice. Write *Past*, *Present*, or *Future* to show the verb tense.

_____ 19. My family is planning a summer vacation.

_____ 20. Last year at this time we were swimming in the Pacific Ocean.

_____ 21. This summer we will be swimming in the Atlantic Ocean.

_____ 22. Our grandfather and grandmother will be going on vacation with us.

_____ 23. Our family was traveling in a motor home to California.

_____ 24. This summer we will be flying on a large jet to the East Coast.

Write the correct progressive form of the verb to complete the sentence.

25. The mechanic _____ the van again tomorrow. **Future**
         repair

26. He _____ the van last week. **Past**
         repair

27. The mechanic _____ the van now. **Present**
         repair

28. Perhaps we _____ a new van soon. **Future**
         need

Choose a progressive verb from numbers 19–28 and use it in your own sentence.

29. _____

_____

Journal

A well-crafted sentence should also have good content.
Sentences may be well-constructed and still have a bad message.

Complete the graphic organizer.

LIES

SWEAR WORDS

CURSES

UNKIND WORDS

GOSSIP

DISRESPECT

CARELESS MISTAKES

PRAYER

TRUE WORDS

KIND WORDS

CLEAR COMMUNICATION

PRAISE

RESPECT

1. What heart attitudes produce bad communication?

_____

_____

_____

_____

_____

_____

2. What heart attitudes produce good communication?

_____

_____

_____

_____

_____

_____

3. What should a writer do to make sure that his sentences are good?

_____

_____

_____

Cumulative Review

Mark the sentence where the underlined word is written correctly.

1. ○ <u>Calvins'</u> bicycle is broken.
   ○ The <u>bicycle's</u> tire is bent.
   ○ He is replacing both <u>tire's</u>.

2. ○ Bianca's two new <u>dress</u> are beautiful.
   ○ The white dress has several pink <u>ribbon's</u>.
   ○ The blue <u>dress's</u> bow is silver.

3. ○ The <u>men's</u> prayer breakfast is Saturday.
   ○ Men from several <u>churches'</u> will be there.
   ○ How many <u>mens</u> are coming to the breakfast?

4. ○ Five brown <u>bunnies'</u> are in the yard.
   ○ The <u>bunnies'</u> tails are white.
   ○ One of the <u>bunnies'</u> is nibbling mom's flowers.

5. ○ Two <u>monkies'</u> are swinging from the branch.
   ○ The little <u>monkey's</u> are twins.
   ○ The <u>monkeys'</u> mother is watching them.

6. ○ A few <u>farmer's</u> still use oxen to farm.
   ○ <u>Oxens</u> can plow fields in the spring.
   ○ Two <u>oxen</u> work together wearing one yoke.

7. ○ Farmers shear their <u>sheeps</u> once a year.
   ○ The <u>sheeps'</u> wool is dyed many colors.
   ○ The <u>sheep's</u> wool made a beautiful sweater.

8. ○ The <u>leaves'</u> colors are brilliant.
   ○ The <u>leave's</u> will soon fall off the tree.
   ○ The <u>leafs'</u> cover the ground.

9. ○ Mrs. <u>Browns'</u> class is singing in the program.
   ○ The two <u>class</u> are in the choir program.
   ○ The <u>class's</u> program is next week.

Mark the stronger reason for the opinion.

10. Carson is the best choice for the school president.
    - ○ I think he is the best choice.
    - ○ He cares for others more than himself.

11. Our class should visit the space museum.
    - ○ The class will learn about space exploration.
    - ○ Our class voted Jupiter as the most unusual planet.

12. The school cafeteria should serve pizza every Friday.
    - ○ I believe that kids will buy pizza.
    - ○ Pizza can be made with healthy toppings such as tomatoes and mushrooms.

Choose a more exact word.

13. Grandma will <u>go</u> to Atlanta today.
    - ○ race   ○ depart   ○ travel

14. What time will her airplane <u>go</u>?
    - ○ race   ○ depart   ○ travel

15. The energetic children <u>go</u> to the car.
    - ○ race   ○ depart   ○ travel

> **go**   *verb*
> to pass from one place to another
> *We* go *to Washington every year.*
> depart, leave, move, proceed, race, run, travel
> **antonym:** stay, remain

Use the thesaurus entry to write a more exact word.

16. <u>Go</u> to the next base. _____

17. We will <u>go</u> soon. _____

18. <u>Go</u> to the front of the line. _____

More Verbs

What would happen if language had no rules?

Literature Link

Excerpt from *Hoop Genius: How a Desperate Teacher and a Rowdy Gym Class Invented Basketball* by John Coy

Naismith tacked the rules to the gym bulletin board and promised the class that if this new game failed, he would not try any more experiments.

Captains chose teams of nine members, and Naismith selected two center men. He tossed the ball up between them, and they jumped for it to start the new game.

Because the men had never played before, Naismith called many fouls for holding, pushing, and tripping. After two fouls, the player had to sit on the sideline until the next goal occurred.

William Chase launched a shot from twenty-five feet . . . that went in for the first and only basket of the game.

When Naismith blew the whistle to end the game, nobody wanted to leave.

Practice

Underline the simple subject once and the action verb twice. Circle the direct object.

1. In the morning, I make my bed.
2. Mother fixes breakfast.
3. I eat the delicious eggs.
4. My sister toasts the bread.
5. Colin pours the orange juice.
6. After breakfast, Father reads the Bible.
7. We all sing a hymn.
8. Joy and I clean the kitchen.
9. Father rides his bike to work.
10. Mother helps me with my lesson.

> To find the direct object, ask *subject + verb what* or *whom*?

Write a direct object to complete each sentence.

11. Micah threw a _____ to his friend.

12. Lee climbed the _____.

13. Mona and Kate found a _____.

14. Several students played _____.

15. The teacher watched the _____.

> Remember that nouns are used as direct objects.

Think of a game that you play with a ball. Write two sentences telling what you might do with the ball. Circle the direct objects in your sentences.

16. _____

_____

_____

Underline the correct verb twice.

17. May I (set, sit) in the front row?

18. Please (lie, lay) the book on the table.

19. I (learned, taught) my memory verse yesterday.

20. Mrs. Jackson (taught, learned) me to read.

21. Jamal (may, can) say his multiplication table.

22. The puppy has (lain, laid) on his blanket a long time.

23. Who (sat, set) the cup on the floor?

24. Father (rose, raised) from his chair and left the room.

25. You (may, can) read your book after recess.

26. Jesus has (risen, raised) from the grave.

Write *C* if the verb used in the sentence is correct. Write *NC* if the verb used is not correct. Use proofreading marks to add the correct verb.

_____ 27. Jack raised his hand quietly.

_____ 28. Miss Mehus learned me how to draw.

_____ 29. Please lie the book on the table.

_____ 30. Sit up straight in your chair.

_____ 31. Can I go out for recess early?

> **Proofreading Marks**
> ∧∨ Add
> ___ꝍ Delete

Write two sentences about one of your parents. Write one sentence using an action verb and one sentence using a linking verb.

32. Action:_____

_____

33. Linking:_____

_____

Journal

An excellent basketball player follows the rules of the game to score points for his team. An excellent writer follows the rules of language to make his or her message clear.

Choose the best word to complete the sentence.

bipeds   humans   mammals   primates

1. _____ are able to use their minds and bodies to follow the complex rules of games and of language.

Think about the word that you chose to complete number 1. How would a different word choice change the meaning of the sentence?

2. _____

_____

Cumulative Review

Mark the best way to write the underlined word or words or choose "No change."

1. The boys <u>play</u> soccer last night.
   - ○ The boys plays soccer last night.
   - ○ The boys played soccer last night.
   - ○ The boys playing soccer last night.
   - ○ No change

2. Emma <u>sing</u> in the community choir next month.
   - ○ Emma sang in the community choir next month.
   - ○ Emma has sung in the community choir next month.
   - ○ Emma will sing in the community choir next month.
   - ○ No change

3. My dad easily <u>swims</u> ten laps.
   - ○ My dad easily swimmed ten laps.
   - ○ My dad easily swum ten laps.
   - ○ My dad easily swim ten laps.
   - ○ No change

4. Mother and Mrs. Banks <u>runned</u> around the track this morning.
   - ○ Mother and Mrs. Banks runs around the track this morning.
   - ○ Mother and Mrs. Banks has ran around the track this morning.
   - ○ Mother and Mrs. Banks ran around the track this morning.
   - ○ No change

5. In the evening, the famous cowboy <u>will ridden</u> the horse in the rodeo.
   - ○ In the evening, the famous cowboy will ride the horse in the rodeo.
   - ○ In the evening, the famous cowboy will rode the horse in the rodeo.
   - ○ In the evening, the famous cowboy ride the horse in the rodeo.
   - ○ No change

6. That photographer <u>has taken</u> my picture before.
   - ○ That photographer has took my picture before.
   - ○ That photographer taked my picture before.
   - ○ That photographer taken my picture before.
   - ○ No change

7. My uncle <u>buy</u> a boat at the Lakeland Boat Show.
   - ○ My uncle buying a boat at the Lakeland Boat Show.
   - ○ My uncle buyed a boat at the Lakeland Boat Show.
   - ○ My uncle will buy a boat at the Lakeland Boat Show.
   - ○ No change

Mark the group of words that is a sentence.

8. ○ Is a collection of tiny water droplets.
   ○ Droplets and crystals in the air.
   ○ Clouds give us clues about the weather.

9. ○ Fog is a cloud that forms close to the ground.
   ○ Water vapor in the warm air.
   ○ Cools close to the ground and condenses.

10. ○ Can grow large and tall and can form thunderclouds.
    ○ Produce thunder and lightning.
    ○ Cumulus clouds are fluffy, cotton-like clouds.

11. ○ Look like the scales on a fish.
    ○ Cirrus clouds are high, thin, wispy clouds.
    ○ Grow as more and more water vapor condenses.

Mark the sentence with a prepositional phrase underlined.

12. ○ Many people in the north helped slaves escape.
    ○ These people organized the Underground Railroad.
    ○ Each person's house was a station.

13. ○ A person who helped the slave was a conductor.
    ○ The conductor would lead groups of slaves to freedom.
    ○ One of the best-known conductors is Harriet Tubman.

14. ○ Harriet Tubman escaped to freedom in the north.
    ○ Harriet had learned how to survive in the woods.
    ○ She knew to follow the North Star to freedom.

15. ○ Once free, Harriet returned to the south to help others.
    ○ People called her Moses because she helped people to freedom.
    ○ Harriet's work for the Underground Railroad was very dangerous.

16. ○ Harriet was successful bringing many slaves to freedom.
    ○ She was married to a free black man.
    ○ John Tubman would not follow Harriet north.

17. ○ Harriet brought over three hundred slaves to freedom.
    ○ She was also a scout for the Union army.
    ○ Harriet Tubman never stopped working to help her people.

Writing a Story

How could fiction be truthful?

Literature Link

Excerpt from *A Day's Work* by Eve Bunting

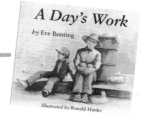

Ben's mustache quivered with anger. "I thought you said your grandfather was a fine gardener. He doesn't even know a *chickweed*?"

Abuelo looked from one of them to the other. "Tell me what is happening, Francisco," he said.

"We left the weeds. We took out the plants," Francisco said softly in Spanish. It was hard to look at his grandfather as he spoke.

Chickweed

"He thought we knew about gardening," Abuelo said. His Spanish was fast and angry. "You lied to him. Isn't that so?"

"We needed a day's work. . . ."

"We do not lie for work."

Now there was more sadness than anger in Abuelo's voice. "Ah, my grandson." He put a hand on Francisco's shoulder. "Ask him

what we can do. Tell him we will come back tomorrow, if he agrees. We will pull out the weeds and put the good plants back."

Francisco felt his heart go weak. "But . . . but Abuelo, that will be twice the work. And tomorrow is Sunday. There is a Lakers game on TV. And there is also church." He hoped the word *church* would perhaps change his grandfather's thinking.

"We will miss them both, then," his grandfather said. "It is the price of the lie. Tell the gentleman what I said and ask him if the plants will live."

Ben said they would. "The roots are still there. If they're replanted early, they'll be all right."

He rubbed his eyes. "This is partly my fault. I should have stayed to get you started. But tell your grandfather I appreciate his offer and I'll bring you back in the morning."

The three of them got in the van.

Francisco sat by the window in huddled silence. He didn't wave to passing cars. He didn't raise his cap. He'd helped his grandfather find work. But in the end the lie had spoiled the day. His throat burned with tears.

Solving Problems

Write the letter of the character from *A Day's Work* by Eve Bunting that matches the description.

_B_ 1. a young boy

_C_ 2. the boy's grandfather

_A_ 3. the man who hires workers to do gardening

A Ben
B Francisco
C Abuelo

Mark the best answer.

4. What is the problem in the excerpt from *A Day's Work*?
   - ○ Ben has not given Abuelo and Francisco enough time to pull all the weeds.
   - ○ Francisco's English is hard for Ben to understand.
   - ● Abuelo and Francisco have pulled the plants instead of the weeds.

5. Why is it hard for Francisco to look at Abuelo as he tells Abuelo that they have done the work incorrectly?
   - ● Abuelo will find out that Francisco has lied.
   - ○ Abuelo thinks he is a fine gardener.
   - ○ The sun is in Francisco's eyes.

6. Why does the story say that "Francisco felt his heart go weak"?
   - ○ Francisco was having a heart attack.
   - ○ Francisco could feel that Abuelo had a weak pulse.
   - ● Francisco began to realize that his lie would have painful consequences.

7. Why is there sadness in Abuelo's voice after he tells Francisco "We do not lie for work"?
   - ○ Abuelo is sad that Francisco got caught.
   - ● Abuelo is sad that Francisco would tell a lie.
   - ○ Abuelo is too tired to stay angry.

8. How does Abuelo offer to solve the problem of the work that was done incorrectly?
   - ● Abuelo tells Francisco to ask Ben if they can redo the work.
   - ○ Abuelo tells Ben that the weeds are prettier than the plants.
   - ○ Abuelo tells Francisco it was Ben's fault they did the work incorrectly.

Ice plants

Read the statement about a character's action in *A Day's Work*. Write *R* if it describes an action that is right and *W* if it describes an action that is wrong.

_W_ 9. Francisco lies to Ben about Abuelo's gardening skills.

_R_ 10. Abuelo corrects Francisco by saying, "We do not lie for work."

_R_ 11. Abuelo offers to do what he can to fix the work that is done incorrectly.

_R_ 12. Ben gives Abuelo and Francisco the opportunity to redo the work.

Choose a statement about a character's action from numbers 9–12. Work with a partner to complete the chart.

13.

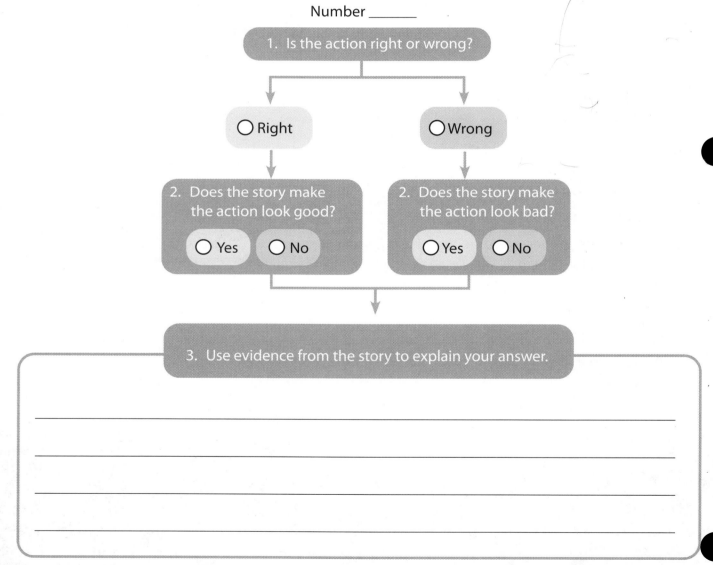

Number _____

1. Is the action right or wrong?

○ Right   ○ Wrong

2. Does the story make the action look good?

○ Yes   ○ No

2. Does the story make the action look bad?

○ Yes   ○ No

3. Use evidence from the story to explain your answer.

Getting an Idea

Writers get ideas for stories in many different ways. Most writers begin with a general idea and then develop that idea as they plan their characters, setting, problem, and solution.

Notice the conversation between the two characters.

Quotation marks show each speaker's exact words.

Writers begin a new paragraph each time there is a different speaker.

Transition words and phrases help make the order of events clear.

The Five-Dollar Bill

One day Ivy was walking down the school sidewalk. She found a five-dollar bill on the ground. "I wonder where this came from," she said. She glanced around, and no one was watching. So she stuffed the money into her pocket. "Maybe I won't tell anyone I found this. I could put it with the money I'm saving for a string-art kit," she thought.

On the way to her classroom, Ivy saw a little kindergarten boy crying. "Hi, Liam. What's wrong?" she asked the boy.

"I lost my money. It was for my teacher's special surprise. My mom's going to be upset," said Liam.

"How much money was it?" asked Ivy.

"Five dollars," said Liam.

Ivy almost didn't say anything about the money she had found. Then she felt ashamed for wanting to keep it.

She dug the bill out of her pocket. "Is this it?" she asked.

When Liam saw the bill, he stopped crying and smiled. "Yes, that's mine!" he said.

"I found it on the sidewalk," said Ivy.

Liam wiped his eyes. "Thank you," he said.

The next day when Ivy got to school, there was a surprise on her desk. It was a thank-you note from Liam's mom and a bag of chocolate cookies!

Brainstorm with a partner to think of ideas from things that have happened to you or to someone you know. Write the ideas in the chart.

Story Ideas

1. A pet disappears. How does the owner find it?
2. Best friends run in a race together. Who wins?
3. A boat begins to sink. What happens to the people on board?
4. A new student seems lonely. How does a classmate help?
5. Children try to surprise their mother on her birthday. Can they do it?
6. The highest scorer on a sports team breaks a leg and can't play. What does the team do?

_____

_____

_____

_____

_____

Write your story idea

What will your story be about?

_Me_____

_____

_____

Planning the Characters

First, decide on a main character for your story. Then use a word web to plan and develop details about the character.

friendly

kind to children

Ivy

4th grader

likes cookies

Identify your main character.

Who will your story be about?

My main character is a _____ named _____.

Complete the word web to help you develop your character. Write the name of your main character in the center oval of the web. Write details about your character in the outside ovals.

tall

loves mist... cake

Mark

the 17 years older ever

player non christian

Planning the Problem, Solution, and Setting

Stories tell about a character with a **problem** that needs to be solved. Once you know some details about your character, you can decide on a problem that fits the character. Then you can plan a **solution** to the problem.

Here is a list of problems the main character of "The Five-Dollar Bill" could have.

Problems for Ivy
Gets in trouble for eating too many cookies
Has a hard spelling test
Finds a five-dollar bill and wants to keep it

The writer chose the problem that fit best with the character.

Problem: Ivy finds a five-dollar bill and wants to keep it.
Solution: She finds out that Liam lost it and gives it to him.

The solution is how the problem will be solved.

How could this fictional story be truthful?
Do right actions look good and wrong actions look bad?

Look at the word web on Worktext page 166 that you used to develop your character. List some problems that your character might have.

He bumped his head on the tree and daus not remember enything.

Choose the problem that fits best with your character. Write the problem and its solution.

What problem will your character have?

Problem: He bumped his head on a tree and lost his memery.

Solution: He gets his memrey back and his head feels beter.

Words and phrases in a story give clues about its **setting**—
when and **where** the story happened.

When? The story "The Five-Dollar Bill" happened in the
daytime.

One day Ivy was walking down the school sidewalk.

Where? All of the action happened at school.

One day Ivy was walking down the school sidewalk.

On the way to her classroom, Ivy saw a little kindergarten
boy crying.

What kind of setting can you imagine your character in?
In what setting could the problem happen?

Times	Places
in the daytime	in the forest
at night	in a rowboat
long ago	in a big city
in the future	in a classroom
in our time	in Alaska

Write a brief description of your setting.

When and where will your story happen?

My story will take place ___at   the   forest___
___in the daytime___

___

___

Planning the Plot

The sequence of events in a story is called the **plot**.

- Stories have a **beginning**, **middle**, and **end**.

- A story's **problem** marks the point at which the story moves from the beginning to the middle.

- The **solution**, or how the problem is solved, marks the point at which the story moves from the middle to the end.

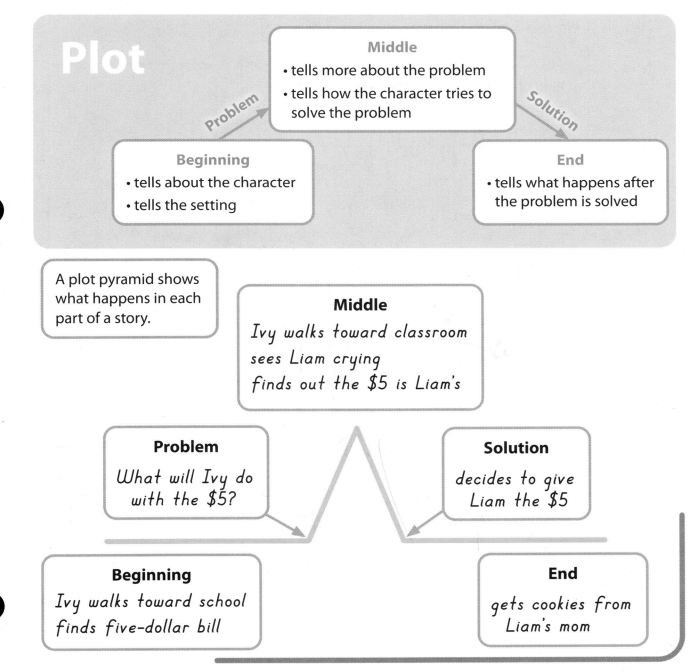

Plot

Middle
- tells more about the problem
- tells how the character tries to solve the problem

Problem →

Beginning
- tells about the character
- tells the setting

Solution →

End
- tells what happens after the problem is solved

A plot pyramid shows what happens in each part of a story.

Middle
Ivy walks toward classroom
sees Liam crying
finds out the $5 is Liam's

Problem
What will Ivy do with the $5?

Solution
decides to give Liam the $5

Beginning
Ivy walks toward school
finds five-dollar bill

End
gets cookies from Liam's mom

Complete the plot pyramid to plan your story's plot.

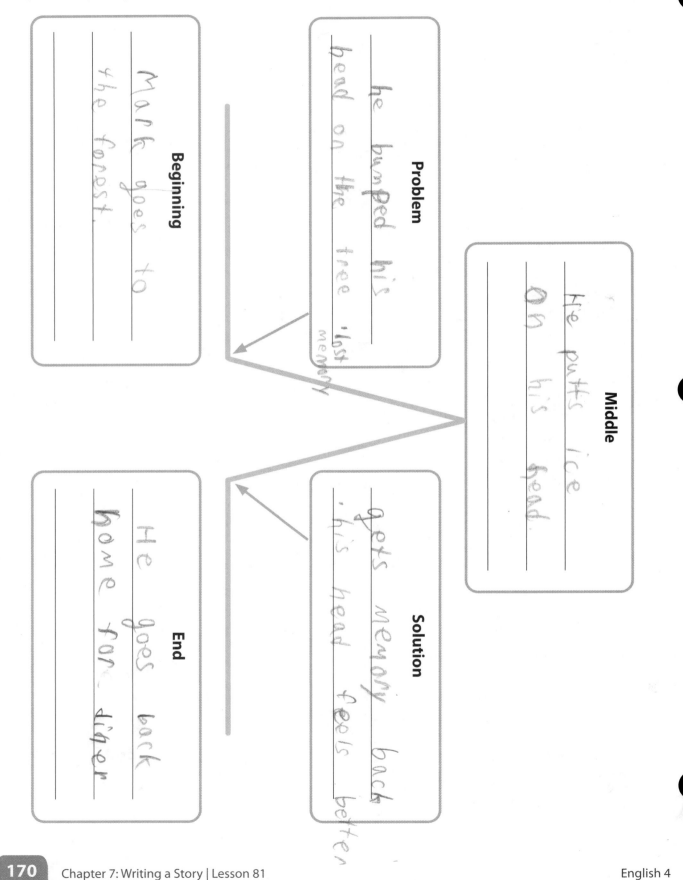

Beginning

Mark goes to the forest.

Problem

he bumped his head on the tree 'lost memory'

Middle

He puts ice on his head.

Solution

gets memory back 'his head feels better'

End

He goes back home for diner

Story: Draft

Draft your story using your planning charts. The spoken words between characters in a story are called **dialogue**. Use dialogue to make your characters more real to the reader.

The Five Dollars

One day Ivy was walking down the school sidewalk. She found a five-dollar bill on the ground. "I wonder where this came from," she said. She looked around, and no one was watching. So She kept walking. "Maybe I won't tell anyone I found this. I could put it with the money I'm saving for a string-art kit," she thought.

On the way to her classroom, Ivy seen a little boy crying. "Hi, Liam. What's wrong?" she asked the boy.

"I lost my money. It was for my teacher's special surprise. My mom's going to be upset," said Liam. Liam was in kindergarten.

"how much money was it?" asked Ivy.

"five dollars," said Liam.

Ivy almost didn't say anything about the money she had found. Then she felt ashamed for wanting to keep it.

She dug the bill out of her pocket. "Is this it?" she asked.

When Liam saw the bill, he stops crying and smiled. "Yes, that's mine! he said.

"I found it on the sidewalk," said Ivy.

Liam wiped his eyes. "Thank you," he said.

The next day when Ivy got to school, there was a surprise on her desk and it was a thank-you note from Liam's mom and a bag of choclat cookies!

Underline the dialogue in the story.

More Transition Words			
first	later	in the meantime	two years ago
then	finally	sometimes	last year
next	when	just then	as soon as
afterward	now	after a while	the next day

Draft your story. Use the drafting guide to check off the parts of the story as you write.

Drafting Guide		
Beginning	Tell about the character and the setting of your story.	
Problem	Tell about your character's problem.	
Middle	Tell more about the problem and how the character tries to solve it.	
Solution	Tell how the character's problem is solved.	
Ending	Tell what happens after the problem is solved.	

Story: Revise

Revise your story. Think about suggestions from your peer conference and use the revising checklist.

> The thesaurus helped the writer find a stronger verb.

> Added words tell what Ivy did with the money right after she found it.

> The writer decided this sentence was in the wrong place. The word *kindergarten* can better describe the boy in an earlier sentence.

The Five-Dollar Bill

One day Ivy was walking down the school sidewalk. She found a five-dollar bill on the ground. "I wonder where this came from," she said. She ~~looked~~ glanced around, and no one was watching. So She ~~kept walking~~ stuffed the money into her pocket. "Maybe I won't tell anyone I found this. I could put it with the money I'm saving for a string-art kit," she thought.

On the way to her classroom, Ivy seen a little kindergarten boy crying. "Hi, Liam. What's wrong? she asked the boy.

"I lost my money. It was for my teacher's special surprise. My mom's going to be upset," said Liam. ~~Liam was in kindergarten.~~

"how much money was it?" asked Ivy.

"five dollars," said Liam.

Ivy almost didn't say anything about the

Continued

money she had found. Then she felt ashamed for wanting to keep it.

She dug the bill out of her pocket. "Is this it?" she asked.

When Liam saw the bill, he stops crying and smiled. Yes, that's mine! he said.

"I found it on the sidewalk," said Ivy.

Liam wiped his eyes. "Thank you," he said.

The next day when Ivy got to school, there was a surprise on her desk and it was a thank-you note from Liam's mom and a bag of choclat cookies!

The last sentence reads better as two sentences.

Use the revising checklist to help you revise your story.

Revising Checklist
The beginning of my story makes you want to keep reading.
My story has a beginning, a middle, and an end.
I included dialogue in my story.
I used colorful words and strong verbs.
I used transition words to make the order of events in my story clear.
My story makes right actions look good and wrong actions look bad.
My story has a satisfying ending.

Proofreading Marks

∧∨	Add
ℯ	Delete
≡	Capital letter
/	Lowercase
↻→	Move

Story: Proofread

Proofread your story to find and correct mistakes.

The Five-Dollar Bill

One day Ivy was walking down the school sidewalk. She found a five-dollar bill on the ground. "I wonder where this came from," she said. She glanced around, and no one was watching. So She stuffed the money into her pocket. "Maybe I won't tell anyone I found this. I could put it with the money I'm saving for a string-art kit," she thought.

On the way to her classroom, Ivy seen a little kindergarten boy crying. "Hi, Liam. What's wrong? she asked the boy.

"I lost my money. It was for my teacher's special surprise. My mom's going to be upset," said Liam.

"how much money was it?" asked Ivy.

"five dollars," said Liam.

> **The word _She_ in this sentence should not be capitalized.**

> **_Saw_ is the correct form of the verb _see_ for this sentence.**

> **A speaker's exact words should begin and end with quotation marks.**

Continued

Ivy almost didn't say anything about the money she had found. Then she felt ashamed for wanting to keep it.

She dug the bill out of her pocket. "Is this it?" she asked.

> The verb should be in the past tense to match other verbs in the paragraph.

When Liam saw the bill, he ~~stops~~ *stopped* crying and smiled. "Yes, that's mine!" he said.

"I found it on the sidewalk," said Ivy.

Liam wiped his eyes. "Thank you," he said.

The next day when Ivy got to school, there was a surprise on her desk. It was a thank-you note

> The writer used a dictionary to correct a misspelled word.

from Liam's mom and a bag of ~~choclat~~ *chocolate* cookies!

Use the proofreading checklist to help you proofread your story.

Proofreading Checklist

I began each sentence with a capital letter.
I ended each sentence with a punctuation mark.
I used capital letters and punctuation correctly in quotations.
I put each speaker's words in a new paragraph.
I used correct verb forms.
I corrected misspelled words.

Proofreading Marks

∧∨ Add
⟋ Delete
≡ Capital letter
⟋ Lowercase
⟜➔ Move

Reflection

> Writers create stories that show how they look at right and wrong.

Think about your story and answer the question.

How does your story make right actions look good and wrong actions look bad?

_____

_____

_____

_____

Cumulative Review

Read the paragraph and complete the activities.

①George Washington was a wise man. ②He <u>were</u> our first president. ③He set a noble example for other presidents to follow. ④President washington valued goodness. ⑤He <u>will respect</u> the Bible. ⑥Washington disagreed with Thomas Jefferson. ⑦Washington <u>encouraged</u> others to do right. ⑧Washington inspired all Americans to be good.

Read the sentence from the paragraph. Choose the best way to write the underlined word or choose "No change."

1. Sentence 2
   - ○ He is our first president.
   - ○ He was our first president.
   - ○ No change

2. Sentence 5
   - ○ He respected the Bible.
   - ○ He respects the Bible.
   - ○ No change

3. Sentence 7
   - ○ Washington encourage others to do right.
   - ○ Washington will encouraged others to do right.
   - ○ No change

Mark the sentence that does not belong in the paragraph.

4. ○ Sentence 3
   ○ Sentence 6
   ○ Sentence 8

Mark the sentence with a capitalization mistake.

5. ○ Sentence 2
   ○ Sentence 4
   ○ Sentence 8

Mark the sentence with the correct verb.

6. ○ Tomorrow we goes on a field trip to a zoo.
   ○ Tomorrow, we went on a field trip to a zoo.
   ○ Tomorrow, we will go on a field trip to a zoo.

7. ○ Today we must completed all of our work.
   ○ Today we must complete all of our work.
   ○ Today we completes all of our work.

8. ○ Last year Pastor and Mrs. Riley will bring our lunches.
   ○ Last year, Pastor and Mrs. Riley bringed our lunches.
   ○ Last year, Pastor and Mrs. Riley brought our lunches.

9. ○ Father and Mother riding on the van with me.
   ○ Father and Mother will ride on the van with me.
   ○ Father and Mother will rides on the van with me.

10. ○ The monkey exhibit is my favorite.
    ○ The monkey exhibit are my favorite.
    ○ The monkey exhibit were my favorite.

11. ○ Zebras and giraffes is together at the zoo.
    ○ Zebras and giraffes lives together at the zoo.
    ○ Zebras and giraffes live together at the zoo.

12. ○ Zebras don't never live with lions.
    ○ Zebras don't live with lions.
    ○ Zebras do'nt live with lions.

13. ○ Pastor Riley drived the church van in the morning.
    ○ Pastor Riley droved the church van in the morning.
    ○ Pastor Riley will drive the church van in the morning.

14. ○ Father and Mother is walking around the zoo with me.
    ○ Father and Mother will walk around the zoo with me.
    ○ Father and Mother will walks around the zoo with me.

15. ○ My mother teached me to be careful around a lion's cage.
    ○ My mother learned me to be careful around a lion's cage.
    ○ My mother taught me to be careful around a lion's cage.

Pronouns

Why should my words serve others?

Adapted from "Robert Moffat," a devotional by Dr. John Dreisbach

I want to tell you the story of a young man who played a very great role in the country of South Africa. It all started in Scotland. An old village pastor was questioned by the deacons of his church. Why had there been no growth in the church, no new members? It seemed the work of the church was at a standstill. They were about to send the pastor away and call a new one.

The deacons said to the old pastor, "No one has come to Christ through your ministry in the past year."

He replied, "Yes, it has been a difficult year, but what about little Bobby?"

The deacons had forgotten about the young boy who had come to Christ that year.

Little Bobby was from a poor but devout Christian family. Some time after his salvation, there was a mission meeting in that village church. An offering was taken. When the offering basket came to little Bobby, he told the usher to put it on the floor.

"I have nothing to give to God but myself," he said, and stepped into the plate with his bare feet.

Bobby really meant it when he gave himself to God for His service. He had little opportunity for education and was apprenticed as a gardener. He learned to love this work and later in life he was called "God's Gardener."

Little Bobby became the outstanding missionary to South Africa—Dr. Robert Moffat, who spent 52 years of his life at Kuruman. He used his gardening skills to benefit the tribal people there. More importantly, he preached Jesus Christ and translated the Bible into that tribal language.

Why do I tell you this story? One young boy from a poor family with little formal education, who gave himself to Christ, was used of God to do mighty things of eternal value. What can God do with your life?

Possessive Pronouns

A **possessive pronoun** replaces a **possessive noun**. Possessive pronouns show that someone has or owns something.

Katelyn's bike is broken.   *Her bike is broken.*

Some possessive pronouns are used before nouns.

My brother is six years old.   *Our house is the one with the green door.*

Some possessive pronouns can stand alone.

That piece of pie is yours.   *Those football tickets are theirs.*

Possessive Pronouns			
Used with Nouns		**Used Alone**	
my	his	mine	his
our	her	ours	hers
your	its	yours	theirs
their			

Underline the possessive pronoun in the sentence.

1. My teacher told the true story of Dr. David Livingstone.

2. His ministry was in Africa more than one hundred years ago.

3. Africa was his mission field.

4. Many Africans gave their lives to Christ because of Dr. Livingstone's ministry.

5. May I borrow your book about David Livingstone?

6. The book isn't mine.

7. I borrowed it for my book report on Monday.

Write the correct possessive pronoun to complete the sentence.

8. Mary Moffat became _____wife.
   David Livingstone's

9. _____ early life was spent in a missionary station in Kuruman, Africa.
   Mrs. Livingstone's

10. The faith of her father, Robert Moffat, became _____.
    Mrs. Livingstone's

11. David and Mary Livingstone met at _____ missionary station.
    the Moffats'

Write two questions that you might ask Dr. Livingstone about his missionary life if he were alive today. Use a possessive pronoun in each question.

12. _____

_____

_____

_____

Underline the possessive pronoun in the sentence.

13. Once, a lion crushed Livingstone's arm with its powerful jaws.

14. The Africans thought their friend would soon be dead.

15. God healed his arm and body while he rested at the mission station in Kuruman.

16. Dr. Livingstone's life is an inspiration for mine.

17. He dedicated his life to serving God always.

18. What will you do with yours?

Write the correct possessive pronoun to complete the sentence.

19. Dr. Livingstone shared information from _____ travels with map makers.
 Dr. Livingstone's

20. The hardships in _____ interior almost ruined Livingstone's health.
 Africa's

21. He often had to be away from his wife and _____ six children.
 Mr. and Mrs. Livingstone's

22. David and Mary believed that no sacrifice was too great for _____ God.
 the Livingstones'

23. Do we have any books about them at _____ house?
 my family's

Confusing Contractions

Homophones are words that sound alike but have different meanings and usually different spellings.

> Some contractions are easily confused with similar contractions or homophones.

> Look carefully at the spelling of the words and at the content of the sentence to help you choose the correct word.

I'd = I had or I would	**they're** = they are
I'll = I will	**there** = that place; location
aisle = a passageway between rows	**their** = possessive pronoun
he's = he is or he has	**he'd** = he had or he would
she's = she is or she has	**she'd** = she had or she would
you're = you are	**its** = possessive pronoun
your = possessive pronoun	**it's** = it is or it has

Underline the correct homophone to complete the sentence.

1. (Their, There, They're) grandmother baked sugar cookies.

2. (I'll, Aisle) give the dog a bath this afternoon.

3. (Its, It's) exciting to ride roller coasters.

4. (Their, There, They're) are twenty-two students in his class.

5. (You're, Your) homework is due on Monday.

6. (Their, There, They're) going to play basketball after school.

7. His seat in church is next to the (I'll, aisle).

8. (You're, Your) going to be late for church.

> What does the word mean in the sentence?

Write the underlined contraction as two words.

_____ 9. It's time to clean your room.

_____ 10. She's been invited to a birthday party this weekend.

_____ 11. He's traveling to Kenya on Thursday.

Write a sentence using the homophone.

12. Their: _____

_____

13. There: _____

_____

14. They're: _____

_____

Underline the correct homophone to complete the sentence.

15. (Your, You're) supposed to practice your instrument every day.

16. Do not stand in the (I'll, aisle) when the bus is moving.

17. Bryson left his watch over (their, there, they're).

18. (It's, Its) crowded in the parking lot at the mall.

> What does the word mean in the sentence?

19. (Their, There, They're) visiting the reptile house at the zoo.

20. (I'll, Aisle) pay for the ice cream sundaes.

21. Take (your, you're) little brother with you to Sunday school.

22. Is (their, there, they're) a game being played tomorrow evening?

23. The bulldog buried (it's, its) bone in the backyard.

Write the underlined contraction as two words.

_____ 24. They're meeting us at the bowling alley at six o'clock.

_____ 25. He's having a birthday celebration.

_____ 26. You're invited to come with us.

_____ 27. I'll bring a present.

_____ 28. He's never blown out all the candles in one breath.

_____ 29. She'd like another piece of cake, please.

Homophones

Homophones are words that sound alike but have different meanings and usually different spellings.

The sky is blue.   *The wind blew the leaves off the trees.*

Homophones								
ate	dear	fair	flower	hair	heal	here	him	hole
eight	deer	fare	flour	hare	heel	hear	hymn	whole
horse	hour	new	nose	not	plain	right	see	stair
hoarse	our	knew	knows	knot	plane	write	sea	stare
pair	sent	to	tail	way	week	wood		
pear	cent	too	tale	weigh	weak	would		
pare	scent	two						

Mark the sentence with the correct homophone.

See Homophones on Handbook pages 379–81.

1. ○ I knew the answer to the question.
   ○ I new the answer to the question.

2. ○ Sailors can make many different kinds of nots.
   ○ Sailors can make many different kinds of knots.

3. ○ The sent of flowers filled the room.
   ○ The scent of flowers filled the room.

Write the homophones correctly to complete the sentence.

would, wood   4. _____ you please stack up the _____?

right, write   5. I _____ with my _____hand.

nose, knows   6. Everyone _____ that an elephant has a long _____.

Write a riddle using a pair of homophones from the chart on Worktext page 199. An example has been done for you.

7.

Why was the horse hoarse?
He had lost his neigh.

Riddle: _____

_____

Answer: _____

_____

Mark the sentence with the correct homophone.

8. ○ How much do the bananas way?
   ○ How much do the bananas weigh?

9. ○ The plain was ready to land on the airstrip.
   ○ The plane was ready to land on the airstrip.

10. ○ Charity rode the Ferris wheel at the fair.
    ○ Charity rode the Ferris wheel at the fare.

11. ○ The mayor's voice was horse after his long speech.
    ○ The mayor's voice was hoarse after his long speech.

What does the word mean in the sentence?

12. ○ It took six weeks for Nathan's broken arm to heal.
    ○ It took six weeks for Nathan's broken arm to heel.

13. ○ I would like to eat a hamburger to.
    ○ I would like to eat a hamburger too.

14. ○ It is not polite to stair at people.
    ○ It is not polite to stare at people.

Write the homophones correctly to complete the sentence.

our, hour   15. _____ photos will be ready in one _____.

pear, pare   16. I will _____ the _____ for the fruit salad.

tail, tale   17. We read a _____ about a donkey without a _____.

see, sea   18. We can _____ the _____ from our hotel room.

eight, ate   19. They _____ dinner at _____.

hymn, him   20. The pastor asked _____ to play a _____.

Indefinite Pronouns

An **indefinite pronoun** does not refer to a specific noun. It refers to an unknown noun or a noun that is not mentioned by name.

Someone sent me a package.

Common Indefinite Pronouns			
anybody	everybody	nobody	somebody
anyone	everyone	no one	someone
anything	everything	nothing	something

Underline the indefinite pronouns in the paragraph.

1.   Everyone is invited to a special service at our church. Our pastor invited someone from Ethiopia to speak to us. After the service, there will be a meal. Anybody can bring an international food to share. I would like to try something from Africa. Last year somebody brought a milk tart from South Africa. A milk tart is a creamy kind of pie made with eggs, milk, and cinnamon. At the end of the meal, there was nothing left in the pie plate, not even crumbs.

Write the best indefinite pronoun to complete the sentence.

everybody   nobody   somebody   something

2. I am trying to learn _____ about the hippopotamus.

3. _____ in my class is researching African animals.

4. _____ in my class has seen a real hippopotamus.

5. _____ told me I can see one at the San Diego Zoo.

Write a sentence using the indefinite pronoun *nobody*, *no one*, or *nothing*.

6. _____

_____

Common Indefinite Pronouns			
anybody	everybody	nobody	somebody
anyone	everyone	no one	someone
anything	everything	nothing	something

Underline the indefinite pronouns in the paragraph.

7.   My cat Ginger ran away last week. Someone forgot to shut the front door. I made a poster with Ginger's picture on it. The poster asked everybody to look for her. I wrote down our phone number so that anyone who found her could call us. For two days, I did not hear anything from anybody. Then on Saturday, the phone rang. Ginger was curled up on somebody's front porch! She was fast asleep. From now on, I will be very careful about closing the front door behind me.

Write the best indefinite pronoun to complete the sentence.

anyone   everyone   everything   nothing

8. _____ in my family enjoys my mom's sourdough bread.

9. _____ can learn to bake homemade bread.

10. _____ in the recipe must be measured accurately.

11. _____ can be left out of the dough.

Write a sentence using the indefinite pronoun *anybody*, *anyone*, or *anything*.

12. _____

_____

Reflexive Pronouns

A **reflexive pronoun** reflects or renames the subject of a sentence.

> Reflexive pronouns are used as direct objects or objects of prepositions.
>
> *The frog saw himself reflected in the pond.*

Reflexive Pronouns	
Singular	**Plural**
myself	ourselves
yourself	yourselves
himself	
herself	themselves
itself	

Underline the reflexive pronouns in the paragraph.

1.   Today my teacher showed us a video about Zambia. The Zambian people are very friendly and enjoy storytelling and sports like soccer and rugby. We learned about some churches in Zambia who built an orphanage for children who had been left by themselves. They knew that Jesus did not keep Himself away from children. Every boy or girl is taught to read the Bible for himself or herself. My classmates and I would like to visit Zambia and introduce ourselves to the children there.

Write the correct reflexive pronoun to complete the sentence.

> itself   myself   themselves

2. A zebra can hide _____ in the tall grass.

3. Giraffes feed _____ by eating leaves from the tops of trees.

4. I took a picture of _____ next to the lemur area at the zoo.

Write a sentence using the reflexive pronoun *ourselves*.

5. _____

_____

Reflexive Pronouns	
Singular	**Plural**
myself	ourselves
yourself	yourselves
himself	
herself	themselves
itself	

Underline the reflexive pronouns in the paragraph.

6.   Have you ever heard of the Queen of Sheba? She may have ruled over the African country called Ethiopia. You can read her story for yourself in the Bible. The queen came to visit King Solomon. She had heard about him and wanted to ask him many questions for herself. I like to imagine myself as part of her caravan. She traveled across the desert with many servants, camels, and gifts for the king. Solomon answered all of the queen's questions and showed himself to be just as wise as the queen had heard.

Write the correct reflexive pronoun to complete the sentence.

> herself   himself   ourselves

7. Elijah quickly packed _____ a lunch on the morning of the field trip.

8. Anna found a seat for _____ at the back of the bus.

9. We entertained _____ with books and games during the long drive.

Write a sentence about a camel. Use the reflexive pronoun *itself*.

10. _____

_____

Relative Pronouns

The **relative pronouns** *who*, *which*, and *that* can be used to combine sentences.

> *The boy* is wearing a red shirt. + *The boy* is my friend. =
> *The boy* who *is wearing a red shirt is my friend.*

> *The cookies* were made with oatmeal and raisins. + *The cookies* are on the table. =
> *The cookies,* which *are on the table, were made with oatmeal and raisins.*

> *The students practiced* the songs. + *The songs* were chosen for the program. =
> *The students practiced the songs* that *were chosen for the program.*

Underline the relative pronouns in the paragraph.

1.   I read a book about a woman who was a missionary to Africa. Her name was Mary Slessor. In 1876, she left Scotland, which had always been her home. She went to the country that is now called Nigeria. Mary's bravery amazed the other missionaries. She visited many places that frightened them. Eventually, the tribes' people learned to trust Mary. They called her their "Ma." Because of Mary, many Nigerian people became followers of Jesus.

Combine the sentences. Use the relative pronoun *who*.

2. Devon has a pen pal. The pen pal lives in Nigeria.

_____

_____

Combine the sentences. Use the relative pronoun *which*.

3. Many people in Nigeria speak English. Nigeria is part of West Africa.

_____

_____

Underline the relative pronouns in the paragraph.

4.   Last week, my family picked peaches at an orchard that is near our house. The man who owns the orchard gave us some baskets to fill. We brought the red wagon to help us carry the fruit. My brother, who is only two years old, rode in the wagon with the peaches. Dad could reach the peaches which were on the highest branches. I picked peaches from the lower branches. Mom will make a pie with the peaches that came from the orchard. Fresh peaches taste delicious!

Combine the sentences. Use the relative pronoun _that_.

5. I like to jump on the trampoline. The trampoline is in the backyard.

_____

_____

Combine the sentences. Use the relative pronoun _who_.

6. My friend can do flips on the trampoline. My friend takes gymnastics lessons.

_____

_____

Combine the sentences. Use the relative pronoun _which_.

7. My dad added a trampoline net. The net keeps us safe when we jump.

_____

_____

Practice

Possessive Pronouns			
Used with Nouns		**Used Alone**	
my	his	mine	his
our	her	ours	hers
your	its	yours	theirs
their			

Underline the possessive pronoun in the sentence.

1. My father bought me a sturdy trail bike.

2. Its tires can handle rocky dirt trails.

3. Father's trail bike is blue like mine.

4. Is your bike a trail bike or road bike?

5. Do you want to ride his bike?

6. I want to ride yours.

Write the correct possessive pronoun to complete the sentence.

7. Zack and Ella rode _____ bikes to the playground.
   <u>Zack's and Ella's</u>

8. Ella pedaled _____ bike toward the swings.
   <u>Ella's</u>

> What pronoun can replace the possessive noun?

9. Zack sped over to see _____ friends.
   <u>Zack's</u>

10. The boys stopped _____ game to see the bike.
    <u>the boys'</u>

Underline the correct homophone to complete the sentence.

11. (Hour, Our) family is having a family reunion.

12. (Here, Hear) is the invitation.

13. (Write, Right) "Turner Family Reunion" on the banner.

14. (Its, It's) next weekend.

15. Are you wearing your (new, knew) shirt?

16. (Their, There, They're) going to the reunion too.

Write the homophones correctly to complete the sentence.

sea, see   17. Would you like to _____ the deep blue _____?

to, two   18. My _____ brothers are going _____ the seashore.

ate, eight 19. Mr. Perez _____ _____ baked clams.

Write the best indefinite pronoun to complete the sentence.

anyone   anything   no one   nothing

20. _____ is more important than playing fair.

21. Would _____ like to play soccer?

22. _____ is better than just sitting around.

23. But _____ wants to be the goalie.

Write the correct reflexive pronoun to complete the sentence.

himself   itself   myself   themselves

24. After the table was set, Mother told the family to help _____.

25. I chose a hamburger for _____.

26. My brother chose a taco for _____.

27. Even our dog found a doggie biscuit for _____.

Write a sentence using the homophone.

28. There: _____

_____

29. Their: _____

_____

Chapter 8 Review

Write the correct pronoun to complete the sentence.

1. _____ is making homemade ice cream.

Mother

2. _____ will be strawberry flavored.

The ice cream

3. We picked _____ ourselves.

the strawberries

4. Dad will show _____ how to pack the ice and rock salt.

my sister and me

5. _____ love homemade strawberry ice cream!

My sister and I

Write the pronoun that replaces the underlined word or words to complete the sentence.

6. <u>Miss Brooks</u> teaches my art class. _____ has blonde hair.

7. Today <u>our class</u> used modeling clay. She reminded _____ to wash our hands first.

8. Zoe chose some blue <u>clay</u>. She made a dolphin out of _____.

Circle the two nouns that the underlined pronoun might replace. Rewrite the second sentence to correct the unclear pronoun.

9. Easton gave Ranger a bowl of dog food. <u>He</u> licked the bowl clean.

_____

Underline the correct word or words to complete the sentence.

10. Liam and (I, me) went fishing at the lake on Saturday.

11. Dad entered (we, us) boys in a fishing contest.

12. The day was fun for (me and Liam, Liam and me).

Underline the simple subject once and the correct verb twice.

13. She (like, likes) pizza with ham and pineapple.

14. I (eat, eats) pepperoni on my pizza.

15. They (make, makes) pizza on Friday nights.

Write the correct possessive pronoun to complete the sentence.

16. _____ mother works at the bank.
    Lucy's

17. She helps set up _____ bank accounts.
    the customers'

18. _____ employees are friendly.
    The bank's

Underline the correct homophone to complete the sentence.

19. (There, Their, They're) going to Kenya next summer.

20. Don't (stare, stair) at the new student.

21. We ate the (hole, whole) watermelon at the picnic.

22. Charlie chose a (plain, plane) bagel and cream cheese for breakfast.

23. Melanie enjoys the (cent, scent, sent) of this candle.

Write the best indefinite pronoun to complete the sentence.

24. Penelope brought cupcakes for _____ in my class.

25. _____ was absent on Thursday.

26. Did you learn _____ from the science lesson?

anything
everyone
nobody

Write the correct reflexive pronoun to complete the sentence.

27. I choose a book for _____ at the library.

28. You may take a bookmark for _____ from the front desk.

29. Abraham Lincoln taught _____ many things by reading books.

30. We will read silently to _____ after lunch.

himself
myself
ourselves
yourself

Write a sentence using the homophone.

31. You're: _____

_____

32. Your: _____

_____

Journal

> A person with strong language skills can use his or her talents in many different kinds of jobs.

Writer

Editor

English Teacher

Lawyer

Journalist

Ambassador

Choose one of the jobs above. How would a person with this job use language skills to do something good?

1. _____

_____

_____

Write a sentence about a way that you plan to use your language skills to do something good this week.

2. _____

_____

_____

_____

Cumulative Review

Read the paragraph and complete the activities.

> ¹ My family raises chickens. ² Dad said, These chickens are the best chickens that we have ever raised." ³ I think he <u>was</u> right. ⁴ Each chicken <u>lays</u> one egg a day. ⁵ My sister and i collect the large brown eggs in the morning. ⁶ We don't never collect fewer than twenty-four eggs. ⁷ Mom fixes eggs for breakfast. ⁸ We <u>eats</u> the fresh brown eggs every day.

Read the sentence from the paragraph. Choose the best way to write the underlined word or choose "No change."

1. Sentence 3
   - ○ I think he <u>am</u> right.
   - ○ I think he <u>is</u> right.
   - ○ No change

2. Sentence 4
   - ○ Each chicken <u>lies</u> one egg a day.
   - ○ Each chicken <u>lain</u> one egg a day.
   - ○ No change

3. Sentence 8
   - ○ We <u>ate</u> the fresh brown eggs every day.
   - ○ We <u>eat</u> the fresh brown eggs every day.
   - ○ No change

Read the question. Mark the sentence that answers the question.

4. Which sentence has a punctuation mistake?
   - ○ Sentence 1
   - ○ Sentence 2
   - ○ Sentence 3

5. Which sentence has a capitalization mistake?
   - ○ Sentence 2
   - ○ Sentence 5
   - ○ Sentence 7

6. Which sentence shows Sentence 6 written correctly?
   - ○ We don't never collect fewer than twenty-four eggs.
   - ○ We dont ever collect fewer than twenty-four eggs.
   - ○ We don't ever collect fewer than twenty-four eggs.

Mark the word that completes the sentence.

7. There aren't ___ cookies left for lunch.   ○ no   ○ any
8. I haven't ___ read that book.   ○ ever   ○ never
9. There isn't ___ that we can do to help him.   ○ nothing   ○ anything
10. I haven't ___ heard a lion roar.   ○ ever   ○ never
11. Hasn't ___ seen my hat?   ○ no one   ○ anyone

Mark the sentence with a prepositional phrase underlined.

12. ○ The chickens scattered and squawked loudly.
    ○ The chickens found safety in the hen house.

13. ○ Life was peaceful in the nearly empty barnyard.
    ○ The aged pony grazed on the lush green grass.

14. ○ Beside the pond the ducklings trailed behind their mother.
    ○ Effortlessly the ducklings glided into the pond.

Mark the word or words that best complete the sentence.

15. _____ is playing the violin in the concert.
    ○ Carter and May
    ○ You
    ○ He

16. On Saturday we ___ .
    ○ at the lake for the whole day
    ○ are going boating on Queen's Lake
    ○ is playing in the tournament

17. Yesterday the construction crew ___ working at a new house.
    ○ is
    ○ was
    ○ be

18. ___ Sims recommended that I stay home from school for a week.
    ○ Dr
    ○ doctor
    ○ Dr.

19. Anthony found a ___ glove on the ground.
    ○ womans
    ○ woman's
    ○ womans'

Adjectives and Adverbs

What makes a sentence beautiful?

Literature Link

Excerpt from *D is for Desert: A World Deserts Alphabet* by Barbara Gowan

Nocturnal begins with the letter N.
It means active at night.
These animals will hunt for food
in the cool desert moonlight.

Great Horned Owl

The desert is awake at night! Summertime temperatures in the Sonoran Desert may drop from 120° Fahrenheit (49° Celsius) at midday to 70° F (21° C) at night. This temperature shift creates dew from the small amount of moisture in the air. Nocturnal animals search for food and avoid predators in the cool, moist darkness.

Nighttime predators usually have large eyes and sensitive ears. The round, yellow eyes of the great horned owl face forward and provide binocular vision and precise depth perception. This stealth hunter flies on silent wings. The oversized ears of the kit fox magnify the sounds of its favorite food, the kangaroo rat. Most bats navigate by echolocation. The bat emits a high-pitched sound that bounces off objects and echoes back to them. Rattlesnakes, scorpions, and most rodents are nocturnal. The jackrabbit, javelina, bobcat, and coyote are nocturnal and also crepuscular (active at dawn and dusk).

Some cacti bloom at night. Each flower blossom has only one night to attract a pollinator. The strong, sweet smell of the queen of the night flower attracts the sphinx moth. Nectar-feeding bats visit the large creamy white saguaro cactus flowers.

Kit Fox

Adjectives

An **adjective** is a word that describes a noun.

Adjectives answer the question ***what kind?*** or ***how many?*** An adjective often comes before the noun that it describes.

Five continents **contain deserts.**   *Large camels* **live in some deserts.**

Predicate adjectives come after the noun that they describe. These adjectives follow a linking verb and describe the subject of the sentence.

Roadrunners **are** *fast*.

Diagram an adjective that comes before a noun on a line that slants below the noun it describes.

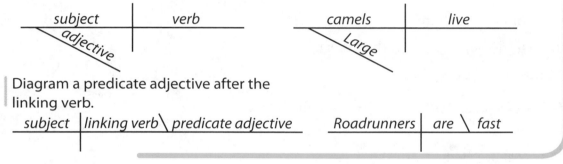

Diagram a predicate adjective after the linking verb.

Circle the adjective that describes the underlined noun. Write *what kind* or *how many* to tell which question the adjective answers.

_____ 1. Some <u>deserts</u> are near the mountains.

_____ 2. Mountains keep rain away from the hot <u>desert</u>.

_____ 3. Strong <u>winds</u> create sand dunes in deserts.

_____ 4. The <u>Sahara Desert</u> is hot.

Circle the adjective. Underline the noun that the adjective describes.

5. Deserts have dry climates.

6. A desert can have temperatures of over a hundred degrees.

7. Cold deserts receive snow instead of rain.

Diagram the simple subject, verb, and adjective in sentence 7.

8. _____

Circle the adjective that describes the underlined noun. Write *what kind* or *how many* to tell which question the adjective answers.

_____ 9. <u>Deserts</u> are interesting.

_____ 10. Many <u>kinds</u> of plants grow in the desert.

_____ 11. These plants store large <u>amounts</u> of water.

_____ 12. Some plants have deep <u>roots</u> to reach water.

_____ 13. Plants with shallow <u>roots</u> take in moisture quickly.

Circle the adjective. Underline the noun that the adjective describes.

14. I have a new book about deserts.

15. Unusual animals live there.

16. Colorful wildflowers bloom in the desert.

17. The wildflowers are beautiful.

Diagram the simple subject, verb, and adjective in the sentence.

18. Sentence 9

_____|_____

19. Sentence 15

_____|_____

20. Sentence 16

_____|_____

21. Sentence 17

_____|_____

Write a sentence that describes the picture above. Circle any adjectives that you use.

22. _____

_____

Articles and Proper Adjectives

The words *a*, *an*, and *the* are special adjectives called **articles**.

Use *a* with singular nouns that begin with a consonant sound.

Use *an* with singular nouns that begin with a vowel sound.

Some words that start with *h* begin with a consonant sound. Others begin with a vowel sound.

a plant   *an animal*

a hat   *an honor*

Use *the* with singular nouns that name a particular person, place, or thing, and with all plural nouns.

the desert   *the Gobi Desert*   *the sand dunes*

A **proper adjective** is an adjective formed from a proper noun. Proper adjectives are always capitalized.

American citizen   *Spanish language*

Write the article *a* or *an*.

1. _____ peanut   2. _____ alligator   3. _____horse   4. _____ igloo

Underline *a*, *an*, or *the* to complete the sentence.

5. (An, The) barrel cactus gets its name from its barrel shape.

6. (A, An) prickly pear cactus has long thorns for protection.

7. (A, An) gel made from the aloe plant is a good medicine.

Underline the proper adjective in the sentence.

8. We visited the Sonoran desert in Arizona.

9. My favorite place to eat is a Japanese restaurant.

Use ≡ to mark the capitalization mistake in the sentence.

10. The ambassador is greek.   11. An italian diplomat greets him at the airport.

Diagram the simple subject, verb, and all of the adjectives in the sentence.

12. The new teacher is Chinese.

Write several sentences about a country you would like to visit. What would you like to do there? What language do the people speak? Circle any proper adjectives that you use.

13. _____

_____

_____

_____

Write the article *a* or *an*.

14. _____ astronaut   15. _____ hour   16. _____ kitchen   17. _____ backpack

Underline *a*, *an*, or *the* to complete the sentence.

18. (A, An) cactus plant can store water.

19. (The, A) sections of a cactus expand during times of rain.

20. The plants get smaller when (the, a) water is gone.

21. (A, An) animal can get water by eating desert plants.

Underline the proper adjective in the sentence.

22. Mom fixed Polish sausage for the missions banquet.

23. Mrs. Abrams made Swedish meatballs.

24. I like Mexican food the best.

25. Stir-fry is a good Chinese dish.

Use ≡ to mark the capitalization mistake in the sentence.

26. We visited an austrian town.

27. I learned some german words from the tour guide.

Diagram the simple subject, verb, and all of the adjectives in the sentence.

28. The American pioneers were brave.

_____|_____

Demonstrative Adjectives

The **demonstrative adjectives** *this*, *that*, *these*, and *those* answer the question **which one?**

Tomorrow, Charlotte will wear this sweater and those shoes.

Demonstrative Adjectives		
	Near	**Far**
Present	this	that
Past	these	those

Circle the demonstrative adjective. Underline the noun that the adjective describes.

1. This store sells all kinds of plants.

2. All of these plants are for sale.

3. That plant is called an elephant bush.

4. Why does it have that name?

5. South African elephants eat those leaves.

6. We can choose one of those containers for our new plant.

7. Let's choose some of these seeds to plant in the flower bed.

8. That hose will help us take care of our garden.

Write a sentence about going shopping. Use a demonstrative adjective in your sentence.

9. _____

_____

Circle the demonstrative adjective. Underline the noun that the adjective describes.

10. This tree is called an ironwood.

11. That name describes the very strong wood from the trees.

12. Look at these carvings made from ironwood.

13. That wood does not float because it is so thick and heavy.

14. In a desert area these trees provide shelter for many plants and animals.

15. Watch out for those thorns on the bark.

16. These leaves feel leathery.

17. In the spring this tree will be covered with pink and purple flowers.

18. Those leaves stay green all year long.

> Look for the word that answers the question *which one?*

Look around the room. Use the demonstrative adjective to write a sentence about objects that you see.

19. This: _____

_____

20. That: _____

_____

21. These: _____

_____

22. Those: _____

_____

Using Adjectives in Sentences

When more than one adjective describes one noun, the adjectives follow a certain order.

Order of Adjectives							
Article/ Number	Opinion	Size/ Shape	Age	Color	Origin	Material	Noun
four		large		green		plastic	turtles
a	delicious				German	chocolate	cake
twelve	diligent		young				students
the	beautiful			white	Bengal		tiger
		rectangular				wooden	boxes

Use different kinds of adjectives to make your sentences more interesting, but avoid using too many adjectives in the same sentence.

Mark the sentence that is written correctly.

1. ○ Ruby Canyon is named after its red beautiful sandstone cliffs.
   ○ Ruby Canyon is named after its beautiful red sandstone cliffs.

2. ○ Visitors can ride into the canyon in large rubber rafts.
   ○ Visitors can ride into the canyon in rubber large rafts.

3. ○ Some people camp overnight on the sandy wide banks of the river.
   ○ Some people camp overnight on the wide sandy banks of the river.

4. ○ Many American adventurous tourists visit the canyon every year.
   ○ Many adventurous American tourists visit the canyon every year.

Write two adjectives to complete the sentence.

5. Be sure to buckle up your _____ life jacket.

6. _____ explorers like to go hiking in the canyon.

7. We will set up the _____ tents on the riverbank.

Order of Adjectives

1. Article and Number
2. Opinion
3. Size and Shape
4. Age
5. Color
6. Origin
7. Material

Mark the sentence that is written correctly.

8. ○ Zoe's mom bought her an exciting new book about animals.
   ○ Zoe's mom bought her a new exciting book about animals.

9. ○ Zoe's favorite ocean animal is the amazing octopus.
   ○ Zoe's ocean favorite animal is the amazing octopus.

10. ○ An octopus has surprising the ability to squeeze itself through small spaces.
    ○ An octopus has the surprising ability to squeeze itself through small spaces.

11. ○ For protection, it can shoot thick black ink at a predator.
    ○ For protection, it can shoot black thick ink at a predator.

12. ○ The long eight arms of the octopus are very strong.
    ○ The eight long arms of the octopus are very strong.

13. ○ Spicy Japanese meat balls are made from octopus meat.
    ○ Japanese spicy meat balls are made from octopus meat.

14. ○ That octopus with the blue pretty spots has a poisonous bite.
    ○ That octopus with the pretty blue spots has a poisonous bite.

15. ○ Squishy little the octopus is the most dangerous kind.
    ○ The squishy little octopus is the most dangerous kind.

Write a sentence about your favorite animal. Use at least two adjectives.

16. _____

    _____

Practice

● Circle the adjective that describes the underlined noun. Write *which one*, *what kind*, or *how many* to tell which question the adjective answers.

_____ 1. Corgis are intelligent <u>dogs</u>.

_____ 2. Corgis herd farm <u>animals</u> such as sheep.

_____ 3. That <u>corgi</u> with the black ears likes to sleep.

_____ 4. They will nip the heels of a fluffy <u>sheep</u> that escapes from the herd.

_____ 5. Many <u>corgis</u> live with families with children.

_____ 6. Children love these <u>dogs</u> as pets.

_____ 7. Aden has two <u>dogs</u>, a corgi and a shepherd.

_____ 8. He and Dory run outside in the warm <u>sunshine</u>.

Underline *a*, *an*, or *the* to complete the sentence.

9. (A, An) corgi wants to please his owner.

● 10. (The, An) owners of corgis are responsible for their dog's care.

11. (The, A) Queen of England owns a corgi.

12. Some say that a corgi has (a, an) attitude of royalty.

13. Does your corgi act like a king or (a, an) queen?

Use ≡ to mark the capitalization mistake in the sentence.

14. Corgis are a welsh dog from Wales in the United Kingdom.

15. The english people are fond of this breed.

16. A swedish cow dog looks like a corgi.

17. The welsh farmers use corgis as herding dogs.

18. Some people who like corgis also might like scottish dogs called Terriers.

19. A favorite irish breed is a Kerry Blue Terrier.

20. The european pet stores sell many types of dogs.

Circle the demonstrative adjective. Underline the noun that the adjective describes.

21. Over many generations, this farm has developed excellent performing dogs.

22. These puppies will be great herding dogs someday.

23. My favorite puppy is that one with its mother.

24. Those puppies in the kennel have already been weaned.

25. That dog with the long hair is also a herding dog.

26. Which one of those breeds do you like best?

> Look for the word that answers the question *which one*?

Look at the things inside your desk. Use the demonstrative adjectives to write a sentence about objects that you see.

27. This/That: _____

_____

28. These/Those: _____

_____

Mark the sentence that is written correctly.

29. ○ What breed is the small black dog?
    ○ What breed is the black small dog?

30. ○ The older Scottish dog is a sheltie.
    ○ The Scottish older dog is a sheltie.

31. ○ A sheltie has long beautiful hair.
    ○ A sheltie has beautiful long hair.

32. ○ The chubby five pups totter after their mother.
    ○ The five chubby pups totter after their mother.

Order of Adjectives

1. Article and Number
2. Opinion
3. Size and Shape
4. Age
5. Color
6. Origin
7. Material

Adverbs

Adverbs describe verbs. They answer **how**, **when**, or **where** something happens. Most adverbs that tell *how* end in *-ly*.

An adverb is not always near the verb that it describes.

When?	*My class* visited *the library* yesterday.
Where?	*The happy children* went inside.
How?	*Each student* quietly chose *a book.*

Diagram an adverb on a line that slants below the verb that it describes.

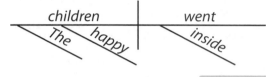

Underline the verb twice. Circle the adverb. Write *how*, *when*, or *where* to tell which question the adverb answers.

_____ 1. The roadrunner quickly caught the rattlesnake.

_____ 2. Gila monsters often live under rocks.

_____ 3. The vulture swooped down from the sky.

_____ 4. The great jerboa sleeps quietly in the daytime.

_____ 5. Tonight the great jerboa will hunt for food.

_____ 6. The small rodent digs busily in the sand.

_____ 7. It searches eagerly for seeds and insects.

Diagram the simple subject, verb, and all the adjectives and adverbs in the sentence.

8. The small jerboa hops gracefully.

9. The sun rose slowly.

Write an adverb that completes the sentence by answering the question in bold.

When? 10. His birthday party is _____

Where? 11. Games will be played _____

How? 12. I wrapped his present _____

Write a sentence about a birthday party. Use an adverb in your sentence.

13. _____

_____

Underline the verb twice. Circle the adverb that describes the verb. Write *how*, *when*, or *where* to tell which question the adverb answers.

_____ 14. Dingoes usually behave like dogs.

_____ 15. The dingo howls loudly in the Australian desert.

_____ 16. It chases sheep and rabbits there.

_____ 17. The fur on its back stands straight in times of fear or anger.

_____ 18. The bearded dragon moves freely across the Australian desert.

_____ 19. This lizard puffs out its beard for protection.

_____ 20. Sometimes its beard turns black.

Diagram the simple subject, verb, and all the adjectives and adverbs in the sentence.

21. A lizard runs fast.

_____|_____
                      |

22. The tiny lizard hatched yesterday.

_____|_____
                      |

Adjectives and Adverbs

An **adjective** is a word that describes a noun. Adjectives answer the question *which one? what kind?* or *how many?*

A tiny baby slept in the crib.   *The air is smoky.*

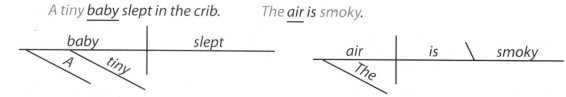

An **adverb** is a word that describes a verb. Adverbs answer the question *how? when?* or *where?*

The motorcycles sped noisily down the road.   *Tonight the three girls will shop for shoes.*

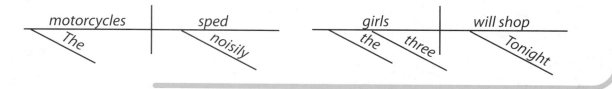

Mark *adjective* or *adverb* for the underlined word.

1. My <u>new</u> folder is on the desk.
   ○ adjective   ○ adverb

2. Mom bought it <u>yesterday</u> at the store.
   ○ adjective   ○ adverb

3. The folder is <u>green</u>.
   ○ adjective   ○ adverb

Underline the adjective and circle the adverb in the sentence.

4. Dexter sometimes eats two sandwiches for lunch.

5. Yesterday his sandwich was big.

6. His kind sister quickly packs their lunches.

7. Dexter carefully pours hot soup into bowls.

Diagram the simple subject, verb, and all the adjectives and adverbs in the sentence.

8. The three kittens purred softly.

Write an adjective or adverb to complete the sentence.

9. The desert sand felt _____ under my feet.

10. The rattlesnake slithered _____ into the shade.

Mark *adjective* or *adverb* for the underlined word.

11. The football team practiced <u>hard</u> before the big game.
    ○ adjective   ○ adverb

12. The <u>excited</u> players listened to their coach.
    ○ adjective   ○ adverb

13. The quarterback ran <u>swiftly</u> with the ball.
    ○ adjective   ○ adverb

14. The team cheered <u>loudly</u> after the winning touchdown.
    ○ adjective   ○ adverb

15. Their uniforms were <u>muddy</u> after the game.
    ○ adjective   ○ adverb

> Does the word describe a noun or a verb?

Underline the adjective and circle the adverb in the sentence.

16. Mom baked three cakes today.

17. Her cakes always taste good.

18. She carefully cuts her chocolate cake.

19. Then she serves large slices for everyone.

Diagram the simple subject, verb, and all the adjectives and adverbs in the sentence.

20. The children ate eagerly.

_____|_____
                 |

21. The delicious cake rapidly disappeared.

_____|_____
                 |

Comparing with -er and -est _____

Adjectives may be used to compare two or more people, places, or things.

Adverbs may be used to compare two or more actions.

| Both adjectives and adverbs use -er and -est to compare.

Add the suffix -er to short adjectives or adverbs that compare sets of two.

An orange is larger than a lemon.   *Skyler ran faster than Damian ran.*

Add the suffix -est to short adjectives or adverbs that compare sets of more than two.

The grapefruit is the largest citrus fruit of all.   *Rowan is the fastest runner in his class.*

Write the -er and -est forms of each adjective or adverb.

1. funny   _____   _____

2. slow   _____   _____

3. cool   _____   _____

Underline the correct adjective or adverb.

4. The temperature in desert regions is (hotter, hottest) than in mountain regions.

5. The cactus is a (sturdier, sturdiest) plant than a pine tree because it stores water.

6. The Sahara is the (larger, largest) desert in the world.

Write the adjective or adverb form to complete the sentence.

7. Vultures fly _____ than roadrunners.

high

8. The roadrunner runs the _____ of any bird in the desert.

fast

9. Roadrunners eat rattlesnakes, even though the snakes are sometimes _____
   than roadrunners.   large

10. I think the roadrunner might be the _____ of all birds.

brave

Write a sentence comparing two animals. Use an adjective or adverb in your sentence.

11. _____

_____

Write the *-er* and *-est* forms of each adjective or adverb.

12. great   _____   _____

13. rainy   _____   _____

14. big   _____   _____

15. late   _____   _____

Underline the correct adjective or adverb.

16. The camel is (larger, largest) than a horse.

17. Camels can survive (long, longer) without water than people can.

18. Horses run (faster, fastest) than camels.

19. Camels are (stronger, strongest) than donkeys.

20. Some countries have contests to find the (prettier, prettiest) camel.

Write the adjective or adverb form to complete the sentence.

21. A camel ride is _____ than a car ride.
                                     bumpy

22. It is _____ for a camel to walk on sand than for a horse.
                   easy

23. Camels have the _____ eyelashes of all desert animals.
                        thick

24. Camels drink the _____ of any mammal.
                     fast

Comparing with *More* and *Most*

Many multi-syllable **adjectives** and **adverbs** compare with *more* and *most*. *More* and *most* are never used with *-er* or *-est* in writing the same word.

> Use **more** with adjectives to compare two people, places, or things.

> Use **most** with adjectives to compare more than two.

> *Mom is a more skillful cook than Dad.*

> *Grandma is the most skillful cook in the family.*

> Use **more** with adverbs to compare two actions.

> Use **most** with adverbs to compare more than two.

Adverbs that end in *-ly* always take *more* and *most*, not *-er* or *-est*.

> *Mom cuts the vegetables more carefully than Dad.*

> *Grandma cuts the vegetables the most carefully.*

Mark the sentence that is written correctly.

1. ○ The most interesting book on the shelf is about desert plants.
   ○ The more interesting book on the shelf is about desert plants.

2. ○ The strawberry hedgehog cactus has the more humorous name.
   ○ The strawberry hedgehog cactus has the most humorous name.

3. ○ It is more colorfuller than the aloe vera plant.
   ○ It is more colorful than the aloe vera plant.

Write the adjective or adverb form to complete the sentence.

4. A cactus grows _____ with dry weather than wet weather.
   easily

5. The spines on a cactus are _____ than the thorns on a rosebush.
   long

6. The cactus with the widest root system can collect water the _____.
   quickly

Write a sentence about a plant. Use an adjective or adverb and with *more* or *most* in your sentence.

7. _____

_____

Mark the sentence that is written correctly.

8. ○ Camels are probably the most famous of all desert animals.
○ Camels are probably the more famous of all desert animals.

9. ○ The Bactrian camel has larger humps than the Arabian camel.
○ The Bactrian camel has the more larger humps than the Arabian camel.

10. ○ Camels were the more useful way to carry heavy loads in the desert.
○ Camels were the most useful way to carry heavy loads in the desert.

11. ○ Some people think that camel meat is more delicious than beef.
○ Some people think that camel meat is most delicious than beef.

12. ○ Camel races are the most popular races in the Middle East.
○ Camel races are the more popular races in the Middle East.

13. ○ Bactrian camels have longest fur than Arabian camels.
○ Bactrian camels have longer fur than Arabian camels.

Write the adjective or adverb form to complete the sentence.

14. Camels are _____ than horses at surviving in the desert.
skillful

15. Items made from camel hair are the _____ in the desert.
plentiful

16. The Sahara desert is the _____ home for dromedary camels.
common

17. This desert has some of the _____ roads in the world.
ancient

Bactrian Camel

Arabian Camel

Forms of *Good* and *Bad*

The words *good* and *well* are often confused in sentences.
Good is always used as an **adjective**. **Well** is an **adverb**
unless it is talking about someone's health.

> *Riley made a good grade on her book report.*
>
> *Cooper plays the piano well.*
>
> *The teacher does not feel well today.*

Special Adjectives That Compare		
One	Two	More than Two
good	better	best
bad	worse	worst

Special Adverbs That Compare		
One	Two	More than Two
well	better	best
badly	worse	worst

Underline the correct adjective form.

1. Mrs. Romano makes the (good, best) spaghetti of anyone I know.

2. I like chocolate cake (better, best) than coconut cake.

3. Alaina's score on the spelling quiz was (worse, worst) this week than last week.

4. That was the (bad, worst) storm we have had in years!

Underline the correct adverb form.

5. He wrote (badly, worst) with his broken arm.

6. Alan ran (worse, worst) in the second race.

7. The singer performed (good, better) after many hours of practice.

8. Sarah likes volleyball the (best, better) of all sports.

Write *good* or *well* to complete the sentence.

9. Dr. Martinez is a _____ doctor.

10. He does his job _____.

11. I am thankful to have a _____ surgeon.

Write a sentence using the word correctly.

12. Good: _____

_____

13. Well: _____

_____

Underline the correct adjective form.

14. The barber gave Nicholas a (good, best) haircut.

15. It was (worst, better) than his last haircut.

16. The last haircut was the (worse, worst) one that he had ever had.

17. It was (worse, worst) than the one Nicholas gave himself.

Underline the correct adverb form.

18. The storm (bad, badly) damaged the roof on our house.

19. He coughed (worse, worst) today than yesterday.

20. An eagle flies (good, better) than a rooster.

21. The trip went (good, well).

22. Nolan is the (good, best) baseball player on our team.

Write *good* or *well* to complete the sentence.

23. They had a _____ time at the birthday party.

24. Corina ran _____ in the race.

25. My parents thanked the pastor for his _____ sermon.

26. Are you a _____ listener?

27. Timothy did his homework _____.

Relative Adverbs

The **relative adverbs** *when*, *where*, and *why* are used to give more information about a **noun**.

In a sentence, a relative adverb introduces a group of words that tells *when*, *where*, or *why*.

George saw the place where the eagles have a nest.

He can see the eaglets during times when their mother is away.

George wonders about the reason why eaglets do not drink milk.

Underline the relative adverb.

1. The Gobi Desert, where many dinosaur fossils are found, is the largest desert in Asia.

2. Snow falls on the sand dunes in the winters when the desert is very cold.

3. Does anyone know the reason why so many dinosaurs are buried here?

4. Roy Chapman Andrews led the expedition in 1920 when the fossils were discovered.

Write the relative adverb *where*, *when*, or *why* to complete the sentence.

5. The round houses _____ many Mongolians live are called yurts.

6. I learned the reason _____ the people build their houses this way.

7. The yurts can be moved at times _____ the people are traveling.

Complete the sentence with your own words.

8. I want to visit a place where _____

_____

9. I would like to know the reason why _____

_____

10. Tomorrow my family is driving to Santa Fe, New Mexico, where my grandmother lives.

11. We will leave early in the morning when it is still dark.

12. The long drive is the reason why we need to leave so early.

13. I will sit next to the window where I can watch the sunrise.

14. My brother will sit in the back seat where he can go back to sleep.

15. We will stop at a restaurant at lunch time when we have been driving for several hours.

Write the relative adverb *where*, *when*, or *why* to complete the sentence.

16. The women went to the tomb _____ Jesus was buried.

17. An angel told them the reason _____ the tomb was empty.

18. The women went back to Galilee _____ they could tell His disciples the news.

19. Jesus appeared to His disciples later that night _____ they were gathered together.

20. All of the disciples were with Jesus on the day _____ He went back to heaven.

21. Jesus sent the disciples into all the world _____ they could tell the good news.

Complete the sentence with your own words.

22. My teacher told us about the time when _____

_____

23. I would like to see the spot where _____

_____

Practice

● Underline the verb twice. Circle the adverb. Write *how*, *when*, or *where* to tell which question the adverb answers.

_____ 1. The school program is tonight.

_____ 2. The choir must arrive early.

_____ 3. They will gather outside.

_____ 4. The families excitedly enter the auditorium to see the program.

_____ 5. The choir sang "The Star Spangled Banner" enthusiastically.

Look for words that answer *how*, *when*, or *where*.

Underline the adjective and circle the adverb in the sentence.

6. The anxious choir walked quickly onto the platform.

7. The boys and girls soon forgot their nervous feelings.

8. They confidently performed the delightful songs.

9. Sweet Stella sang her solo last.

10. Mother sat somewhere in the large crowd.

● Write the adjective or adverb form to complete the sentence.

11. Treyvon is the _____ boy in the choir.
                        tall

12. The boys in the choir walk _____ than the girls.
                                    quick

13. Stella's mother was the _____ mother in the auditorium.
                                happy

14. The choir was glad to sing the _____ song last.
                                        easy

15. I ate the _____ of the two pieces of cake during the choir party.
                    big

Mark the sentence that is written correctly.

16. ○ Field Day is the most popular event at school.
    ○ Field Day is the popularest event at school.

17. ○ The three-legged race is the more exciting activity for everyone.
    ○ The three-legged race is the most exciting activity for everyone.

18. ○ In this race, the girls ran more quicklier than the boys.
    ○ In this race, the girls ran more quickly than the boys.

19. ○ The children in the sack race were more competitive than those in the ring toss.
    ○ The children in the sack race were most competitive than those in the ring toss.

20. ○ Our principal was the determinedest competitor in the pie eating contest.
    ○ Our principal was the most determined competitor in the pie eating contest.

Underline the correct adjective form.

21. Mrs. Jenkins was the (worse, worst) softball player.

22. However, she was the (better, best) sport on the field.

23. My friend played a (bad, worse) game as a pitcher.

Underline the correct adverb form.

24. It was sad that Candon hurt his arm (badly, worse) when he fell off the swing.

25. Cassandra played (worse, worst) in the morning than in the afternoon.

26. My class is (better, best) at softball than soccer.

Write *good* or *well* to complete the sentence.

27. Alonso was not feeling _____ today.

28. My team played _____ in the giant volleyball game.

29. Roshan is a very _____ player.

Write the relative adverb *where*, *when*, or *why* to complete the sentence.

30. I lost my phone on the athletic field _____ the official stands.

31. The reason _____ I can't locate my phone is that hundreds of people are on the field.

32. I will search for the phone this evening _____ Field Day is over.

33. I will start by looking in the place _____ I was sitting.

Chapter 9 Review

Circle the adjective that describes the underlined noun. Write *which one*, *what kind*, or *how many* to tell which question the adjective answers.

_____ 1. Dustin is looking for new <u>rocks</u> for his collection.

_____ 2. We found three <u>pebbles</u> on the playground.

_____ 3. This <u>rock</u> is large, and that one is small.

_____ 4. These rocks have smooth <u>surfaces</u>.

_____ 5. Dustin's favorite one has black <u>stripes</u> on it.

_____ 6. This <u>rock</u> came from the desert of New Mexico.

Underline *a*, *an*, or *the* to complete the sentence.

7. Amaya got (a, an) new fish tank for her birthday.

8. She put (a, an) underwater castle in the tank.

9. (A, The) fish enjoy hiding in the castle.

Use ≡ to mark the capitalization mistake in the sentence.

10. Mom enjoys italian food.

11. I like greek food better.

12. Every year american tourists visit Italy and Greece.

13. Which european country would you like to visit?

Mark the sentence that is written correctly.

14. ○ We will fly a large American flag on the flagpole.
    ○ We will fly an American large flag on the flagpole.

15. ○ The tiny fifty white stars represent the fifty states.
    ○ The fifty tiny white stars represent the fifty states.

16. ○ Raise the flag all the way to the top of the tall metal pole.
    ○ Raise the flag all the way to the top of the metal tall pole.

Underline the verb twice. Circle the adverb that describes the verb.

17. Gwen and Gina will swim at the pool today.

18. Gwen swims fast in swimming races.

19. The girls walk carefully around the edge of the pool.

20. They dry themselves quickly before leaving.

Underline the correct adjective or adverb.

21. This math book is (bigger, biggest) than that science book.

22. Which school subject do you think is the (harder, hardest) of all?

23. Alexander can do math problems (faster, fastest) than I can.

Mark the sentence that is written correctly.

24. ○ The pie tasting contest is the most popular booth at the fair.
    ○ The pie tasting contest is the more popular booth at the fair.

25. ○ The cherry pie was more deliciouser than the apple pie.
    ○ The cherry pie was more delicious than the apple pie.

26. ○ Pumpkin pie was bought most frequently than the cherry pie.
    ○ Pumpkin pie was bought more frequently than the cherry pie.

27. ○ Aunt Adeline's blueberry pie had the most outstanding crust.
    ○ Aunt Adeline's blueberry pie had the more outstanding crust.

Underline the correct adjective or adverb form.

28. Everly is a (good, well) softball player.

29. Everly scored many points in her (better, best) game.

30. She hopes her team will play (good, well) this year.

31. The cut on Jose's arm hurt (bad, badly) yesterday.

32. The cut looks (worse, worst) today.

33. I hope the cut will get (good, well) soon.

Write a sentence comparing two foods. Use an adjective or adverb in your sentence.

34. _____

_____

Journal

Imagine that you have been visiting the desert in this picture. Choose a friend or family member and write a postcard to tell that person about your trip. Use adjectives and adverbs in your note.

> God cares about beautiful things. We can honor God by talking and writing about the wonderful things He has made.

Cumulative Review

Mark the pronoun that best completes the sentence.

1. Mother and __ prayed together.
   - ○ her
   - ○ me
   - ○ I

2. The girls played __ violins well.
   - ○ they
   - ○ hers
   - ○ their

3. Three boys sang with __ girls.
   - ○ we
   - ○ us
   - ○ they

4. My pastor preached to __.
   - ○ them
   - ○ they
   - ○ their

Mark the pronoun that replaces the underlined word or words.

5. Mr. Puerta fixed snacks for the team.
   - ○ His
   - ○ He
   - ○ Him

6. Mr. Puerta coaches the players after school.
   - ○ they
   - ○ his
   - ○ them

7. Patrick kicked the ball into the goal.
   - ○ its
   - ○ it
   - ○ it's

8. The coach smiled at Patrick's goal.
   - ○ its
   - ○ his
   - ○ their

Mark the sentence that is written correctly.

9. ○ "Would you like to go rock climbing?" asked Father.
   ○ "Would you like to go rock climbing," asked Father?

10. ○ "Sure, I would love to go, said Oliver!"
    ○ "Sure, I would love to go!" said Oliver.

11. ○ "Can Barrett go with us"?
    ○ "Can Barrett go with us?"

12. ○ "If his parents approve, he can go with us."
    ○ "If his parents approve, He can go with us."

13. ○ "Are we going to the Climb high Gym in Jonesville?"
    ○ "Are we going to the Climb High Gym in Jonesville?"

14. ○ Father said, "We will go to the Gym in North Adams."
    ○ Father said, "We will go to the gym in North Adams."

Read the paragraph and complete the activities.

> [1] Have you ever been afraid of the dark at night! [2] You will not ever be afraid of the dark in heaven. [3] There is no night their. [4] God covers Hisself with light. [5] God will be the light in heaven. [6] Believers will live in the light of God's presence. [7] God made everything good. [8] For all eternity, you will not be afraid of the dark!

Read the sentence from the paragraph. Choose the best way to write the sentence or choose "No change."

15. Sentence 1
    - ○ Have you ever been afraid of the dark at night.
    - ○ Have you ever been afraid of the dark at night?
    - ○ No change

16. Sentence 2
    - ○ You willn't never be afraid of the dark in heaven.
    - ○ You will not never be afraid of the dark in heaven.
    - ○ No change

17. Sentence 3
    - ○ There is no night they're.
    - ○ There is no night there.
    - ○ No change

18. Sentence 4
    - ○ God covers Him self with light.
    - ○ God covers Himself with light.
    - ○ No change

Mark the best way to combine sentence 5 and sentence 6.

19. ○ God will be the light in heaven believers will live in the light of God's presence.
    - ○ God will be the light in heaven and believers will live in the light of God's presence.
    - ○ God will be the light in heaven, and believers will live in the light of God's presence.

Mark the sentence that does not belong in the paragraph.

20. ○ Sentence 6
    - ○ Sentence 7
    - ○ Sentence 8

Writing a Tall Tale

What makes a good hero?

"Pecos Bill Rides a Twister"
Retold by Bethany Davis

The people of Texas had a problem. They hadn't had a drop of rain for months. It was so dry that all the toads hopped away looking for water. One afternoon, Pecos Bill found a dead rattlesnake in his yard.

"Look, Widder Maker," he said to his horse. "This here snake done choked on the dust."

Bill was worried. Soon all the crops would wither up and die, just like the rattlesnake. He looked up at the clouds creeping across the big Texas sky and wondered what he could do to help.

Suddenly, he had an idea. He saddled up Widow Maker and rode out looking for a twister. He found a big one hovering over Kansas. As that twister came a-spiralin' down, Bill swung his lasso and caught it right in the middle.

"Yee-haw!" Bill yelled. He jumped onto that storm's back and held on tight.

That twister didn't like having Bill on its back, not one bit. It let out a big crack of thunder. Widow Maker ran home. He didn't like thunder. But Bill hung on.

The twister bucked and rolled like a bronco. Luckily, Bill was the best bronc rider west of the Mississippi. He rode that twister right across Kansas, through Oklahoma, and all the way back to Texas.

At last, the twister gave up. It turned into a great big rainstorm that rolled across the whole southwest and finally dumped Bill in California. As he tumbled down from the clouds, his spurs scratched out a new valley. You can still see this valley today. Folks call it Death Valley.

Bill had to walk home, but he was pleased. That rainstorm was just in time to save the crops.

Tall Tale Characters

Read the statement that describes a character's action in "Pecos Bill Rides a Twister." Write the character's name in the blank.

Pecose bill 1. catches a twister with a lasso

widow maker 2. helps the main character find a twister

widow maker 3. runs home when he hears thunder

Pecos bill 4. tumbles down from the clouds

Write the name of the main character of "Pecos Bill Rides a Twister" in the center oval of the word web. Write details about the character in the outside ovals.

5.

cowboy

brave

Pecos bill

helpful

good with laso

Mark the best answer.

6. What is the problem in "Pecos Bill Rides a Twister"?
   ○ Rattlesnakes live too close to Pecos Bill's house.
   ◉ The people of Texas need rain.
   ○ A big twister is destroying whole states in the West.

Write the solution to the problem in "Pecos Bill Rides a Twister."

7. Solution: He rode a twister intel it becam to rain to watered the crops

Write one of Pecos Bill's good qualities in the chart. Then write an action from the tall tale that shows Bill using that quality in a good way.

Good Quality	Good Action
hei is brave becas he hangs on the twister	

Tall Tales

A **tall tale** is a story about a larger-than-life hero. No one is expected to believe a tall tale.

> The tale uses exaggeration to make the reader laugh.

> Colorful descriptions bring pictures to the reader's mind.

A tall tale hero is usually bigger, stronger, or smarter than anyone else.

Humor often comes from making the characters and their problems bigger and more dramatic than what they would be in real life.

The Biggest Bee in the South

It was a hot summer morning in Georgia. Tom Toughguy was enjoying breakfast out on his porch. Every morning Tom ate five hundred biscuits dripping with honey. He was just about to pop the last three biscuits into his mouth when he heard a terrible sound like a chainsaw.

"Whoa!" he yelled. "That there bee's the biggest one I ever seen!"

A gigantic bee was flying toward him. It was buzzing so loudly that Tom had to cover his ears. The bee was bigger than an elephant. Its stinger was as long as a telephone pole. That bee was furious because Tom had used so much honey from its hive.

Tom flung his orange juice at the bee. That would have drowned most bees, but it just made this one madder. The bee zoomed over the porch rail.

Continued

"You won't get me!" shouted Tom. Then he shook out his big red napkin and threw it over the bee's head. Quick as a lightning flash, he tied the napkin's edges in a knot.

The bee was blindfolded! It flew in crazy circles around the yard. It slammed into Tom's house. It smacked into a tree.

Tom grabbed his knife and chopped off the bee's stinger. That made the bee so upset that it flew to Antarctica. Tom chopped the stinger up into pieces and stacked them in a woodpile fifty feet tall. Neighbors for miles around heated their homes with that firewood all the next winter.

Exaggeration describes something as larger or more interesting than it really is.

Write *T* next to events that could happen only in a tall tale. Write *R* next to events that could happen in real life.

_R_ 1. A small boy crushes an ant beneath his shoe.

_T_ 2. A man stops a giant from stepping on his house.

_T_ 3. A girl blows out a forest fire by herself.

_R_ 4. A cat leaps up on a piano.

_T_ 5. A boy walks across the United States in one hour.

_R_ 6. A woman cleans a house in one day.

_R_ 7. A girl wins a cookie-baking contest.

_T_ 8. A woman rides a catfish down a river.

_T_ 9. A man leaves a footprint the size of a lake.

_R_ 10. A bird flies to the next town.

Think of another event that could happen only in a tall tale. Write a sentence describing the event.

11. _Once there was a boy named TimTim he was a giant and always crushes stufe in tow_

Planning the Hero and Other Characters

The **hero** is the main character of a tall tale. A tall tale hero can do impossible things.

> *Pecos Bill lassos a twister and rides it until it turns into a rainstorm.*

> *Paul Bunyan, a gigantic logger, takes mile-long steps.*

Use the questions to help you plan your hero. Check off each question as you think about it. Complete the information about your hero.

The Hero

- ☐ Will your hero be a man, a woman, a girl, or a boy?
- ☐ To what could you compare your hero's size?
- ☐ To what could you compare your hero's brainpower?
- ☐ To what could you compare your hero's strength?
- ☐ What impossible acts will your hero be able to do?
- ☐ Does your hero have good qualities that could be used in a good way?

My hero is a ___7 year old boy___ named ___Bob___

My hero is as big as ___17 ft. tall. as tall as the E.___

My hero is as smart as ___the smartest person alive.___

My hero is as strong as ___hulk and captin americas sheild___

My hero can ___use his supur tranoformor to transform a moon___

My hero has the good quality of ___bravery to usfump lo ofcpa a___ ___glir robot___

_____

_____

Most tall tales include other characters besides the hero. They may be people or animals.

Pecos Bill's horse, Widow Maker, takes him hunting for a twister.

In another tall tale, Pecos Bill marries Slewfoot Sue. Other characters are the preacher who marries them, the other cowboys, and his horse.

Paul Bunyan's big blue ox, Babe, drinks an entire river dry.

Sally Ann Thunder Ann Whirlwind rescues and marries Davy Crockett. Later she tosses alligators away from their house to protect their son, Hardstone.

Plan more characters for your tall tale. Write the name of a character in the center oval of the word web. Write details about that character in the outside ovals.

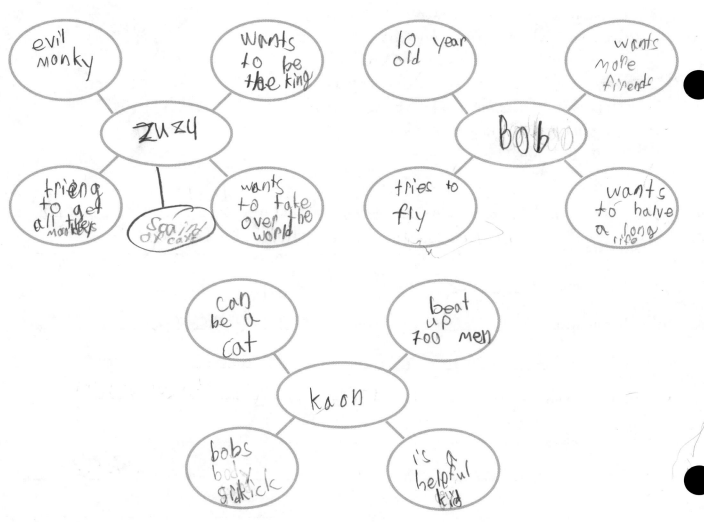

Planning the Problem, Solution, and Setting

In a tall tale, the hero battles a powerful enemy. This struggle is usually called the **problem**.

> *Pecos Bill struggles with a twister.*

> *Tom Toughguy battles a gigantic bee.*

The **solution** to the problem is usually an impossible act performed by the hero.

> *Pecos Bill rides the twister until it turns into a rainstorm.*

> *Tom Toughguy blindfolds the gigantic bee and chops off its stinger.*

Tom's problem is introduced near the beginning of the story.

He was just about to pop the last three biscuits into his mouth when he heard a terrible sound like a chainsaw.

"Whoa!" he yelled. "That there bee's the biggest one I ever seen!"

A gigantic bee was flying toward him. It was buzzing so loudly that Tom had to cover his ears.

Possible Problems

1. A hailstorm threatens to flatten the hero's town.
2. A pack of wolves surrounds the hero's campground at night.
3. A lion escapes from the zoo and ends up in the hero's backyard.
4. A giant tidal wave rushes toward the hero's beachside home.
5. A group of international thieves steal some jewels in the hero's city.

What type of problem would fit with your hero?

What impossible act could your hero do to solve the problem?

Choose a problem from the list above or make up your own. Write your problem and its solution.

Problem: _Zuzu is trieng to take over the world_

Solution: _Bob telles kaon and kaon killes him with his cat powers_

The **setting** of a tall tale is the **time** and **place** in which the story happens. Many tall tales happen in particular places.

Stories about Pecos Bill take place in the West.

Stories about Paul Bunyan take place in the North.

The story about Tom Toughguy takes place in the South.

Make sure your tall tale's problem goes with its setting. For example, some problems and places would not fit together.

Problem: *a forest fire*

Setting: *the North Pole*

Problem: *a dust storm*

Setting: *the continent of Antarctica*

Problem: *a whale trying to overturn a ship*

Setting: *the Mexican desert*

Problem: *a mountain rockslide*

Setting: *the plains of Kansas*

> What is the problem in your tall tale?
>
> In what type of setting would it fit best?

Times	Places
midnight	Yellowstone National Park
early morning	a busy city street
in our time	the desert
long ago	the Austrian Alps
in your grandparents' time	the moon

Write a brief description of your setting.

Time: _midnight at 1982 May 5th_

Place: _Desertian_

Planning the Plot

The tall tale is a particular kind of story. The sequence of events in any story is called the **plot**.

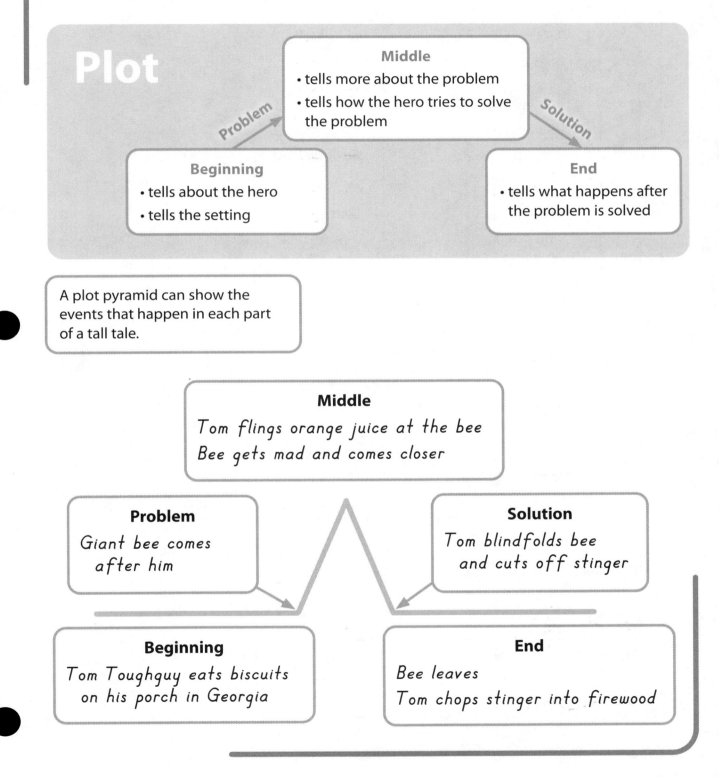

A plot pyramid can show the events that happen in each part of a tall tale.

Plot

Beginning
• tells about the hero
• tells the setting

Middle
• tells more about the problem
• tells how the hero tries to solve the problem

Problem

Solution

End
• tells what happens after the problem is solved

Middle
Tom flings orange juice at the bee
Bee gets mad and comes closer

Problem
Giant bee comes after him

Solution
Tom blindfolds bee and cuts off stinger

Beginning
Tom Toughguy eats biscuits on his porch in Georgia

End
Bee leaves
Tom chops stinger into firewood

Complete the plot pyramid to plan your tall tale's plot.

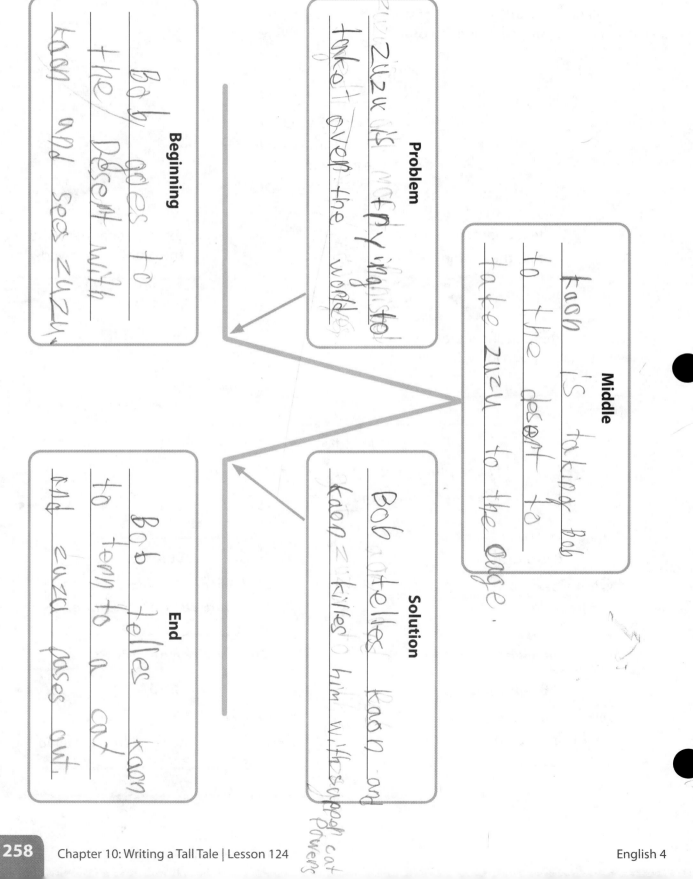

Beginning

Bob goes to the Desert with toon and sees zuzu.

Problem

Zuzu is trying to take over the world.

Middle

Kaon is taking Bob to the desert to take Zuzu to the cage.

Solution

Bob atelles kaon and kaon kills him with supough cat powers.

End

Bob telles kaon to torn to a cat and zuzu pases out.

Tall Tale: Draft

Draft your tall tale using your planning charts.
Write your story as if you were telling it out loud.
Use quotation marks to show dialogue.

> The hero and setting appear early in the story.

> The character's spoken words sound like a real person talking.

> Colorful words create pictures in the reader's mind.

The Biggest Bee in the South

It was a hot summer morning in georgia. Tom Toughguy was enjoying breakfast out on his porch. Every morning Tom ate five hundred biskits with honey on them. He was just about to pop the last three biskits into his mouth when he heard a terrible sound.

"Whoa!" he shouted. "That there bee's the biggest one I ever seen!

A big bee was flying toward him. It was buzzing so loudly that Tom had to cover his ears. The bee was bigger than an elephant. It's stinger was really long. That bee was mad because Tom had used so much honey from it's hive.

Tom flung his orange juice at the bee. That would have drowned most bees, but it just made this one madder. The bee zoomed over the porch rail.

Continued

> Transition words help make the order of events clear.

"You wont get me!" shouted Tom. Then Tom shook out his big red napkin and threw it over the bee's head. He tied the napkin's edges in a not.

The bee was blindfolded! It flew in circles around the yard.

Tom grabbed his knife and chopped off the bee's stinger. That made the bee so upset that it flew to Antarctica. Tom chopped the stinger up into pieces and stacked them in a woodpile fifty feet tall.

More Transition Words

first	later	in the meantime	two years ago
then	finally	sometimes	last year
next	when	just then	as soon as
afterward	now	after a while	the next day

Draft your tall tale. Use the drafting guide to check off the parts of the tall tale as you write.

Drafting Guide

Beginning	Tell about the hero and the setting of your tall tale.	
Problem	Tell about your hero's problem.	
Middle	Tell more about the problem and how the hero tries to solve it.	
Solution	Tell how the hero's problem is solved.	
Ending	Tell what happens after the problem is solved.	

Tall Tale: Revise

Revise your tall tale. Think about suggestions from your peer conference and use the revising checklist.

Colorful words make the reader see and hear details in the story.

The writer found interesting synonyms in the thesaurus.

A simile can describe the stinger here.

The Biggest Bee in the South

It was a hot summer morning in georgia.

Tom Toughguy was enjoying breakfast out on his porch. Every morning Tom ate five hundred

dripping

biskits with honey ~~on them~~. He was just about

to pop the last three biskits into his mouth

like a chainsaw

when he heard a terrible sound.

yelled

"Whoa!" he ~~shouted~~. "That there bee's the

biggest one I ever seen!

gigantic

A ~~big~~ bee was flying toward him. It was

buzzing so loudly that Tom had to cover his

ears. The bee was bigger than an elephant.

as long as a telephone pole   furious

It's stinger was ~~really long~~. That bee was ~~mad~~

because Tom had used so much honey from it's

hive.

Tom flung his orange juice at the bee. That

would have drowned most bees, but it just

made this one madder. The bee zoomed over the

porch rail.

Continued

"You wont get me!" shouted Tom. Then ~~Tom~~ *he*

shook out his big red napkin and threw it

Quick as a lightning flash,
over the bee's head. He tied the napkin's edges

in a not.

crazy
    The bee was blindfolded! It flew in circles
It slammed into Tom's house. It smacked into a tree.
around the yard.

    Tom grabbed his knife and chopped off

the bee's stinger. That made the bee so upset

that it flew to Antarctica. Tom chopped the
Neighbors for miles around used that firewood to heat
stinger up into pieces and stacked them in a
their homes all the next winter.
woodpile fifty feet tall.

> A pronoun replaces the proper noun *Tom* to keep it from being repeated too often.

> The writer decided to exaggerate Tom's speed.

> Added details show how the bee acted.

> A new sentence tells how Tom used his strength and brainpower to help others.

Use the revising checklist to help you revise your tall tale.

Revising Checklist
The beginning of my tall tale gives the hero and the setting.
My tall tale has a beginning, a middle, and an end.
My tall tale has a clear problem and solution.
I included dialogue in my tall tale.
I used colorful descriptions and exaggeration.
The hero of my tall tale has good qualities used in a good way.
My tall tale has a satisfying ending.

Proofreading Marks

∧∨	Add
ℯ	Delete
≡	Capital letter
/	Lowercase
⟳→	Move

Tall Tale: Proofread

Proofread your tall tale to find and correct mistakes.

> **Proper nouns should be capitalized.**

> **The writer used a dictionary to check spelling.**

> **The possessive pronoun does not use an apostrophe.**

The Biggest Bee in the South

It was a hot summer morning in georgia. Tom Toughguy was enjoying breakfast out on his porch. Every morning Tom ate five hundred *biscuits* ~~biskits~~ dripping with honey. He was just about to pop the last three *biscuits* ~~biskits~~ into his mouth when he heard a terrible sound like a chainsaw.

"Whoa!" he yelled. "That there bee's the biggest one I ever seen!"

A gigantic bee was flying toward him. It was buzzing so loudly that Tom had to cover his ears. The bee was bigger than an elephant. *Its* ~~It's~~ stinger was as long as a telephone pole. That bee was furious because Tom had used so much honey from *its* ~~it's~~ hive.

Tom flung his orange juice at the bee. That would have drowned most bees, but it just made this one madder. The bee zoomed over the porch rail.

Continued

> The writer checked for correct use of contractions.

> A good proofreader can find homophones used incorrectly.

"You won't get me!" shouted Tom. Then he shook out his big red napkin and threw it over the bee's head. Quick as a lightning flash, he tied the napkin's edges in a ~~not~~ *knot*.

The bee was blindfolded! It flew in crazy circles around the yard. It slammed into Tom's house. It smacked into a tree.

Tom grabbed his knife and chopped off the bee's stinger. That made the bee so upset that it flew to Antarctica. Tom chopped the stinger up into pieces and stacked them in a woodpile fifty feet tall. Neighbors for miles around used that firewood to heat their homes all the next winter.

Use the proofreading checklist to help you proofread your tall tale.

Proofreading Checklist

I began each sentence with a capital letter and ended it with a punctuation mark.
I used capital letters and punctuation correctly in quotations.
I put each speaker's words in a new paragraph.
I used contractions correctly.
I used pronouns correctly.
I corrected misspelled words.

Proofreading Marks

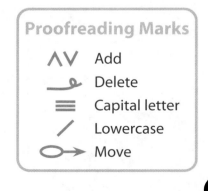

∧∨ Add
⟋ Delete
≡ Capital letter
╱ Lowercase
⟶ Move

Reflection

> This plot summary gives an idea for a different tall tale about Pecos Bill and a twister.

Pecos Bill wants to get back at some people in another town. First, he lassos a twister. Next, he rides it over to the lake that provides the town's water supply. He holds the twister in place until it sucks every drop of water from the lake. Then Bill steers the twister toward the town. He tightens the lasso. Soon the lake water gushes out of the twister and washes the town away.

Answer the questions about the tall tale plot summary.

1. What kind of hero would use his strength in this way?

_____

_____

2. Is this a hero we should admire? Explain your answer.

_____

_____

_____

_____

Cumulative Review

Read the paragraph and complete the activity.

⟨1⟩Last night, dad received an emergency alert.⟨2⟩A tornado <u>touch</u> down in our area.⟨3⟩The weather service <u>see</u> signs of a tornado.⟨4⟩Our family <u>runs</u> to a safe place.⟨5⟩We <u>heard</u> the spinning sounds of the tornado.⟨6⟩We <u>waits</u> a long time in the basement.⟨7⟩The tornado caused a lot of damage, but we were thankful that no one got hurt.

Read the sentence from the paragraph. Choose the best way to write the sentence in the past tense or choose "No change."

1. Sentence 2
   ○ A tornado touched down in our area.
   ○ A tornado touches down in our area.
   ○ No change

2. Sentence 3
   ○ The weather service sees signs of a tornado.
   ○ The weather service saw signs of a tornado.
   ○ No change

3. Sentence 4
   ○ Our family run to a safe place.
   ○ Our family ran to a safe place.
   ○ No change

4. Sentence 5
   ○ We hear the spinning sounds of the tornado.
   ○ We hears the spinning sounds of the tornado.
   ○ No change

5. Sentence 6
   ○ We waited a long time in the basement.
   ○ We wait a long time in the basement.
   ○ No change

Mark the pronoun that best replaces the underlined noun or nouns.

6. <u>Chloe</u> needs new shoes for school.
   - ○ You
   - ○ She
   - ○ He

7. <u>Mother and Chloe</u> went to the mall.
   - ○ You
   - ○ She
   - ○ They

8. Mother found shoes for <u>Chloe</u> in the store.
   - ○ her
   - ○ she
   - ○ you

9. Mother tried on a pair of shoes for <u>Mother</u>.
   - ○ she
   - ○ her
   - ○ herself

10. The store clerk thanked <u>Mother and Chloe</u>.
    - ○ they
    - ○ them
    - ○ you

Mark the sentence with the pronoun used correctly.

11. ○ I walked around the track with Katie.
    ○ Me walked around the track with Katie.

12. ○ Us enjoyed walking and talking together.
    ○ We enjoyed walking and talking together.

13. ○ I and Katie are the same age.
    ○ Katie and I are the same age.

14. ○ The teacher often walks with we girls.
    ○ The teacher often walks with us girls.

15. ○ The teacher tells Katie and me stories.
    ○ The teacher tells Katie and I stories.

More Sentences

11

What are some ways that language can be broken?

Literature Link

"Angel Island Light Station" Excerpt from *Safely to Shore: America's Lighthouses* by Iris Van Rynbach

Angel Island, California • Built 1886

The Angel Island Light Station was first established as a fog-bell signal station. The 4,000-pound fog bell was the largest in service at the time and was sounded by an automatic striking machine. Most machines would strike for 10,000 blows with one winding. But at fogged-in Angel Island, the fog bell averaged two blows every 15 seconds—11,520 rings per day! The striking machine had to be wound twice each day if the fog did not clear.

In 1906 Juliet Nichols was keeper of Angel Island Light Station. One day thick fog rolled into San Francisco Bay, and Juliet rushed to turn on the fog signal. But the striking machine broke down after only a few minutes. Juliet stared out into the fog. She could just make out the sound of slapping waves on a ship's hull. There was no time to fix the equipment, so Juliet grabbed a hammer and started pounding the fog bell. The ship heard the signal and veered away from the dangerous coast. Juliet was exhausted, but she knew she couldn't stop until the fog lifted. For 20 hours and 35 minutes, she struck the bell over and over until her arm ached and her ears rang. Juliet kept the Angel Island Light Station for 12 years. Her courage and dedication saved countless lives.

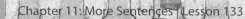

Prepositions Review

A **phrase** is a group of words that work together, but it does not have both a subject and a verb.

A **prepositional phrase** begins with the **preposition** and ends with a noun or pronoun that works as the **object of the preposition**.

> **On Saturday** Christopher set up a lemonade stand **in the front yard**.
>
> *On Saturday Christopher set up a lemonade stand in the front yard.*

Common Prepositions					
about	around	beside	in	on	to
above	at	by	inside	out	under
across	before	down	near	outside	until
after	behind	for	of	over	up
along	below	from	off	through	with

Underline the prepositional phrases.

1. The first American lighthouse was built in 1716.

2. There are many interesting stories about this lighthouse.

3. It was built in Boston Harbor.

4. It was destroyed by the British in the Revolutionary War.

5. The Americans rebuilt it after the war.

6. This lighthouse has had about sixty different keepers.

7. At the first American lighthouses, the keepers burned whale oil, kerosene, or lard oil in the lamps.

8. The keeper spent most of his day tending to the lamps in the lighthouse.

Underline the prepositional phrases.

9. Many lighthouses are made of brick.

10. Tower-shaped lighthouses have many steps leading to the top.

11. I read a story about lighthouses.

12. The keeper and his family lived beside the lighthouse.

13. At the top of the tower, the lighthouse keeper tended the lights.

14. One night he saw the shape of a sinking ship.

15. The lighthouse keeper ran quickly down the stairs.

16. He rowed his boat across the choppy waves.

17. The keeper pulled the struggling men to safety.

18. Without the help of the lighthouse keeper, the men would have died.

Describe what your day might be like if you were a lighthouse keeper one hundred years ago. Circle the prepositions that you use.

19. _____

_____

_____

_____

Using Commas in Sentences

Writers often use a **comma** to show a pause in writing. If a sentence is read aloud, the reader should pause at a comma to help the listener understand what is being said.

Using Commas

1. Add commas in a series.

   In gym class today we walked, ran, and skipped around the playground.

2. Use commas with nouns of direct address.

   Allison, do you know the answer?

   Welcome to our class, Jameson!

   When you leave the room, Erik, please turn off the lights.

3. Add a comma after introductory words such as **yes**, **no**, and **well**.

   Well, people often make mistakes with punctuation.

   Yes, I will check my work carefully.

4. Use a comma after long introductory phrases of five or more words.

   In the early morning hours, Mom got up to make a birthday breakfast.

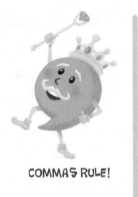

COMMAS RULE!

Mark the sentence that is written correctly.

1. ○ Before the surprise birthday party, we went to the grocery store.
   ○ Before the surprise, birthday party we went to the grocery store.

2. ○ May we have vanilla ice cream, Mom?
   ○ May we have vanilla ice cream Mom?

3. ○ In first grade I learned, about hammerhead sharks.
   ○ In first grade I learned about hammerhead sharks.

Use ⋀ to insert a comma where it is needed.

4. No you may not eat cookies before breakfast.

5. After the toddler's long nap he was happy.

6. Finish your homework Zachary and then you may go outside.

7. Addison saw jellyfish starfish and seahorses at the aquarium.

Write a sentence using *yes*, *no*, or *well* at the beginning of the sentence.

8. _____

_____

Write a sentence using a person's name in a direct address.

9. _____

_____

Mark the sentence that is written correctly.

10. ○ Did you know, Samuel that the first lighthouse was built in Ancient Egypt?
    ○ Did you know, Samuel, that the first lighthouse was built in Ancient Egypt?

11. ○ Well, this book tells more about the history of lighthouses.
    ○ Well this book tells more about the history of lighthouses.

12. ○ Lighthouses today are usually built of stone, wood, brick, or steel.
    ○ Lighthouses today are usually built of stone, wood, brick or steel.

Use ⋀ to insert a comma where it is needed.

13. Luna did you learn anything at school today?

14. Well we watched a video about sea turtles.

15. A sea turtle can use its flippers to swim crawl and dig.

16. In the soft sand on the seashore a mother turtle digs a hole for her eggs.

17. Yes it is very difficult for the baby turtles to survive.

18. Could we visit the sea turtles at the aquarium Mom?

Independent Clauses

A **clause** is a group of words that has a **subject** and a **predicate**.

An **independent clause** has a **subject** and a **predicate**. It expresses a complete thought and can stand alone. It is a simple sentence.

> *Many lighthouses are open to the public.*

A **fragment** is a group of words that does not express a complete thought. Some fragments are missing either a subject or a predicate.

> *The tower on the lighthouse.*

> *Built on the rocks.*

Mark whether the group of words is an independent clause or a fragment.

1. The Split Rock Lighthouse overlooks Lake Superior.
   ○ independent clause   ○ fragment

2. A storm in November of 1905.
   ○ independent clause   ○ fragment

3. Twenty-nine shipwrecks in one night.
   ○ independent clause   ○ fragment

4. The president of the U.S. Steel company went to Washington, D.C.
   ○ independent clause   ○ fragment

5. Asked Congress to build a lighthouse.
   ○ independent clause   ○ fragment

6. The lighthouse was finished in 1910.
   ○ independent clause   ○ fragment

Write an independent clause by adding a subject or a predicate to the fragment.

7. The lighthouse on the cliff.

   _____

8. Sailed carefully around the rocks.

   _____

Mark whether the group of words is an independent clause or a fragment.

9. Tourists often visit the Great Lakes.
   ○ independent clause   ○ fragment

10. Lake Superior is one of the five Great Lakes.
    ○ independent clause   ○ fragment

11. The world's largest freshwater lake.
    ○ independent clause   ○ fragment

12. Eighty types of fish live in these waters.
    ○ independent clause   ○ fragment

13. Went trout fishing last summer.
    ○ independent clause   ○ fragment

14. Located between Minnesota and Ontario.
    ○ independent clause   ○ fragment

15. Parts of the lake freeze in the winter.
    ○ independent clause   ○ fragment

16. Rarely freezes completely.
    ○ independent clause   ○ fragment

17. Copper, iron, and silver mines near the lake.
    ○ independent clause   ○ fragment

Write an independent clause by adding a subject or a predicate to the fragment.

18. The fisherman in the plaid shirt.

_____

19. Cooked the fish over the campfire.

_____

Write an independent clause about an animal that you might find at a lake.

20. _____

_____

Dependent Clauses

A **clause** is a group of words that has a **subject** and a **predicate**.

An **independent clause** expresses a complete thought and can stand alone. It is a simple sentence.

> *Kobe has new roller skates.*

A **dependent clause** has a **subject** and a **predicate** but cannot stand alone as a sentence. It does not express a complete thought.

| Some fragments are dependent clauses.

| A **subordinating conjunction** is a joining word used at the beginning of a dependent clause.

> ***Because*** *Kobe has new roller skates.*

Common Subordinating Conjunctions

after	because	until
although	since	when

Write *IC* if the clause is independent or *DC* if the clause is dependent. Circle any subordinating conjunction.

> Can the clause stand alone?

_____ 1. White cliffs are near Cape Blanco Lighthouse.

_____ 2. Because "blanco" means "white" in Spanish.

_____ 3. Although it is not near a harbor.

_____ 4. The lighthouse warned ships away from the dangerous coast.

_____ 5. It is the tallest lighthouse in Oregon.

_____ 6. Since the lighthouse is still standing.

_____ 7. Many tourists visit each year.

_____ 8. James Langlois was the keeper for forty-two years.

Think about what it would be like to build a lighthouse on rocky land. Write an independent clause explaining one of the difficulties or dangers that a construction crew might face.

9. _____

_____

Write *IC* if the clause is independent or *DC* if the clause is dependent.
Circle any subordinating conjunction.

_____ 10. After World War II started.

_____ 11. The Cape Blanco Lighthouse protected the mainland.

_____ 12. Since the United States was fighting in the war.

_____ 13. The lighthouse became an army headquarters.

_____ 14. The Japanese plane was not noticed.

_____ 15. When the enemy planned an attack.

_____ 16. The lighthouse escaped damage.

_____ 17. Although bombs fell into the forest nearby.

_____ 18. Until the war ended.

_____ 19. The lighthouse returned to its original purpose.

More Dependent Clauses

Some **fragments** are dependent clauses. One way to correct a fragment that is a dependent clause is to remove the subordinating conjunction.

Common Subordinating Conjunctions		
after	because	until
although	since	when

Fragment ⟶ *Since the captain saw the lighthouse*

Sentence ⟶ *The captain saw the lighthouse.*

Write *IC* if the clause is independent or *DC* if the clause is dependent. Rewrite any dependent clause as an independent clause.

_____ 1. When my family visited Washington State last year.

_____

_____ 2. We went hiking on the trails around Cape Flattery Lighthouse.

_____

_____ 3. Many tourists visit Washington State.

_____

_____ 4. Because the coast of the Pacific Ocean is very beautiful.

_____

_____ 5. I enjoyed walking on the beach.

_____

_____ 6. Until the sun began to set.

_____

Write *IC* if the clause is independent or *DC* if the clause is dependent.
Rewrite any dependent clause as an independent clause.

_____ 7. The Cape Flattery Lighthouse had several different keepers.

_____

_____ 8. Because the lighthouse was built on an island.

_____

_____ 9. Since visitors did not come often.

_____

_____ 10. The keepers were frequently unhappy living at the lighthouse.

_____

_____ 11. One day the keepers became angry with each other.

_____

_____ 12. When they began to fight.

_____

_____ 13. The lighthouse keeper threw hot coffee at his assistant.

_____

Think about how God wants Christians to solve their disagreements. Complete the
dependent and independent clauses in this sentence.

Matthew 22:39
Thou shalt love thy neighbour as thyself.

14. When _____ ,

God wants me to _____ .

Complex Sentences

A **subordinating conjunction** joins a dependent clause to an independent clause to form a **complex sentence**.

Common Subordinating Conjunctions		
after	because	until
although	since	when

Use a comma after a dependent clause if it comes at the beginning of a complex sentence.

After art class is over, I will help my teacher clean the brushes.

I enjoy each class because I always learn new things.

COMMAS FIRST!

COMMAS RULE!

Write a subordinating conjunction to complete the sentence.

1. Abbie Burgess lived at Matinicus Rock _____ her father was the lighthouse keeper.

2. Abbie acted bravely _____ a terrible storm came.

3. _____ her father was away, Abbie and her family were alone on the island.

4. Abbie brought her family and her chickens into the lighthouse

   _____ the storm passed.

5. _____ their house was destroyed, they were safe inside the lighthouse.

Rewrite the sentences using a subordinating conjunction to combine them. Add a comma if necessary.

6. Several ships sailed safely through the storm. Abbie kept the light burning.

   _____

   _____

7. The storm was over. People praised Abbie's courage.

   _____

   _____

Common Subordinating Conjunctions		
after	because	until
although	since	when

Write a subordinating conjunction to complete the sentence.

8. _____ all of the birds on Matinicus Island are interesting, the puffins are my favorite.

9. Puffins are easy to recognize _____ they have bright orange beaks.

10. _____ lighthouse keepers are no longer needed to run Matinicus Rock Lighthouse, scientists use the building as a research station.

11. The island is closed to visitors _____ the birds are nesting.

Rewrite the sentences using a subordinating conjunction to combine them. Add a comma if necessary.

12. Soccer practice is canceled today. It is raining.

_____

_____

13. We will have our next practice. The field is dry.

_____

_____

14. I have extra free time. I will play a board game with my brother.

_____

_____

Use a comma if the dependent clause comes at the beginning of the sentence.

Practice

Mark the sentence that is written correctly.

1. ○ On the beach I collected polished stones seashells and a shark's tooth.
   ○ On the beach I collected polished stones, seashells, and a shark's tooth.

2. ○ May I keep them Mom?
   ○ May I keep them, Mom?

3. ○ Yes, you can use the collection for your science project.
   ○ Yes you can use the collection for your science project.

Use ⋀ to insert a comma where it is needed.

4. Dad Mom and Maci found a sand crab buried in the sand.

5. Well that is a great find!

6. While digging in the sand they discovered the sand crab.

7. I wonder Maci if the sand crab was afraid when it saw you!

Mark whether the group of words is an independent clause or a fragment.

8. Many different hermit crabs, purple urchins, and sea anemones.
   ○ independent clause   ○ fragment

9. You must return the little animals to the sea after you catch them.
   ○ independent clause   ○ fragment

10. A small octopus crawled along the tide pool.
    ○ independent clause   ○ fragment

11. Swimming, surfing, and boating on the hot summer day.
    ○ independent clause   ○ fragment

Write an independent clause by adding a subject or a predicate to the fragment.

12. The ring-billed seagull.

_____

13. Build sand castles at the seashore.

_____

Write *IC* if the clause is independent or *DC* if the clause is dependent.
Rewrite any dependent clause as an independent clause.

_____ 14. My granddad taught me how to fish.

_____

_____ 15. Because we fished from his boat.

_____

_____ 16. After I caught my first fish!

_____

_____ 17. I am thankful that my granddad took me fishing.

_____

Common Subordinating Conjunctions		
after	because	until
although	since	when

Write a subordinating conjunction to complete the sentence.

18. _____ bass fish are plentiful, many people fish for bass.

19. My grandmother always has a fish fry _____ granddad and I go fishing.

20. I want to win a bass fishing contest _____ I grow up.

Rewrite the sentences using a subordinating conjunction to combine them. Add a comma if necessary.

21. Grandmother baked the cornbread. She fried the fish.

_____

_____

22. I wanted Granddad to eat the biggest fish on the platter. I love my granddad.

_____

_____

Chapter 11 Review

Mark the sentence that is written correctly.

1. ○ Can I help you wash the car Dad?
   ○ Can I help you wash the car, Dad?

2. ○ I will bring the bucket, soap, and sponge.
   ○ I will bring the bucket soap, and sponge.

3. ○ Yes, I can turn on the water.
   ○ Yes I can turn on the water.

Use ⋏ to insert a comma where it is needed.

4. Bryce would you like to learn Spanish?

5. Well Mrs. Gonzalez can teach you.

6. After school on Friday afternoons Mrs. Gonzalez's class will meet in Room 104.

7. Molly Julian and Adrian have already signed up for her class.

Mark whether the group of words is an independent clause or a fragment.

8. Caden wants to go whale watching this summer.
   ○ independent clause   ○ fragment

9. The whales with the black and white patches.
   ○ independent clause   ○ fragment

10. Caden read an article about orcas.
    ○ independent clause   ○ fragment

11. Also called killer whales.
    ○ independent clause   ○ fragment

Write an independent clause by adding a subject or a predicate to the fragment.

12. Live in the Pacific Ocean.

_____

13. Caden and his classmates.

_____

Write *IC* if the clause is independent or *DC* if the clause is dependent.
Rewrite any dependent clause as an independent clause.

_____ 14. Olivia enjoys computer class.

_____

_____ 15. Because Mrs. Walker is a good teacher.

_____

_____ 16. The students need to practice every day.

_____

_____ 17. Until they can type without looking at their hands.

_____

Common Subordinating Conjunctions

after	because	until
although	since	when

Write a subordinating conjunction to complete the sentence.

18. _____ my class went to the library, I found a book about whales.

19. _____ they live under water, whales come to the surface to breathe.

20. People used to hunt whales _____ whale fat was useful for making whale oil.

21. Baby whales usually stay with their mothers for several years _____ they are born.

Rewrite the sentences using a subordinating conjunction to
combine them. Add a comma if necessary.

22. Will finished his homework quickly. He wanted to use his new skateboard.

_____

_____

23. Will is a good student. Sometimes he needs to ask for help.

_____

_____

Journal

George does not enjoy writing and grammar. He makes lots of mistakes on his English papers. George's teacher says that he should keep trying to do better. George doesn't think that grammar and spelling are very important. He says that he doesn't care if he gets bad grades and he doesn't want to keep trying. He thinks that people will figure out what he means even if he makes mistakes.

Answer the questions about the paragraph.

1. Do you agree with George? Why or why not?

_____

_____

_____

2. What do you think George should do next?

_____

_____

_____

3. What do you plan to do to improve your language skills?

_____

_____

_____

Cumulative Review

© BJU Press. Reproduction prohibited.

● Read the sentence. Place parentheses around any prepositional phrase. Then diagram the sentence.

1. Cameron threw the ball.

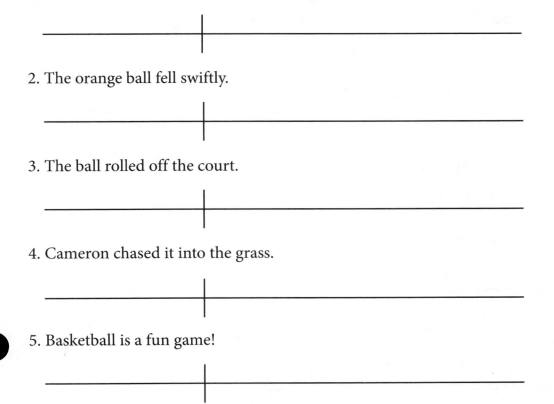

2. The orange ball fell swiftly.

3. The ball rolled off the court.

4. Cameron chased it into the grass.

● 5. Basketball is a fun game!

Mark the best way to combine the sentences.

6. The Webbs have a betta fish. The Webbs have a parrot.
   ○ The Webbs have a betta fish the Webbs have a parrot.
   ○ The Webbs have a betta fish and a parrot.

7. I like to catch monarch caterpillars. I like to watch monarch caterpillars.
   ○ I like to catch and watch monarch caterpillars.
   ○ I like to catch monarch caterpillars and I like to watch monarch caterpillars.

8. Bradley gave his dog a bath. Terrell gave his dog a bath.
   ○ Bradley and Terrell gave their dogs baths.
   ○ Bradley gave his dog a bath and Terrell did too.

9. Kent's snake eats in its cage. Kent's snake sleeps in its cage.
   ○ Kent's snake eats in its cage and sleeps in its cage too.
   ○ Kent's snake eats and sleeps in its cage.

Mark the sentence that is written correctly.

10. ○ The Bible tells us that King Solomon was the most wise man that ever lived.
    ○ Methuselah was the oldest man recorded in the Bible.
    ○ Esther was the beautifulest woman in the land of Persia.

11. ○ Peter, James, and John was followers of Jesus.
    ○ During a storm, Peter walk on water to Jesus.
    ○ James and John were fishermen and brothers.

12. ○ Brought little children to Him.
    ○ The woman and little children.
    ○ Jesus took the children into His arms.

13. ○ My father taught me to pitch.
    ○ Mrs. Evans teached me to catch.
    ○ Mr. Mackey learned me to run the bases.

14. ○ Luka and he is going to a summer camp.
    ○ His bags is packed and ready to go.
    ○ They are spending the week at the camp.

15. ○ He don't eat no junk food.
    ○ There wasn't no one to buy healthy snacks.
    ○ He will not eat any potato chips.

Mark the sentence with the correct end punctuation.

16. ○ The name of my basketball team is the Richmond Rockets.
    ○ Our team has played well this season?
    ○ Are we going to the youth basketball playoffs!

17. ○ Tyrell is our point guard!
    ○ Can he make three-pointers?
    ○ Wow, watch him shoot.

18. ○ Coach Davis tells us to listen to the referee?
    ○ Coach wants us to do our best.
    ○ He has taught us many basketball drills!

19. ○ Basketball begins with drills and practice!
    ○ The drills perfect your skill as a player?
    ○ We practice many hours before playing in a game.

20. ○ Tyrell runs quickly down the court?
    ○ Will he jump for a layup.
    ○ Tyrell scores!

When do differences matter?

Literature Link

Excerpt from *Peanut Butter Friends in a Chop Suey World* by Deb Brammer

Dear Dawn,

How are you? I miss you! I've been in Taiwan for less than two weeks, but so much has happened already.

First of all, this necklace is for you to remember me by. I bought it at the market all by myself in Chinese! I wish you could see the market. It looks like one huge garage sale. You can buy anything there. Well, not chocolate chips or peanut butter, but you can buy them at special stores. They just cost a lot more. Taiwan has all kinds of fruits that I've never even heard of. I didn't know what half of the food at the market was.

It's really different here. You know how I told you I thought Taiwan would be a lot like California? Big cities and lots of people? Well, the cities are big, but not in the same way. I can't explain it. Everything is just so different from America.

I think I'll learn a lot here. I can see how Chinese people live, and I'm going to learn to speak their language. I don't know much so far, but I'm just getting started. I've spoken to several Chinese people. You wouldn't believe how brave I've been.

Of course I don't like ALL of the differences. Some things aren't as fun here. But I keep reminding myself that I'm not here to have fun. Missionaries win souls, and there's plenty of them to win. Amy Carmichael was brave and I will be too. Really.

Don't worry about me. I already have a few friends, but you'll always be my best friend.

Next time I'll tell you about my school and the church and our neighborhood. Write soon.

Your best friend forever,
Amy Carmichael Kramer

Comparing and Contrasting

Comparing is telling how two things are alike.

Contrasting is telling how they are different.

My twin sisters, Ella and Eva, look very much alike. They both have curly, brown hair and blue eyes. They are also exactly the same height. They both wear glasses, and they both have braces on their teeth. Sometimes they even dress alike. Almost everyone has trouble telling them apart.

Even though Ella and Eva look alike, their personalities are very different. Ella is daring and loves water sports. She likes people, and she is not afraid to try new things. She is always making us laugh. In contrast, Eva is more of a bookworm. She is quieter than Ella and more serious, but she likes to laugh at Ella's jokes. She loves babies and animals, and she is very good at tennis.

This **Venn diagram** shows the likenesses and differences between the twins.

Ella | Eva

daring
loves water sports
likes people
tries new things
makes us laugh

blue eyes
same height
curly brown hair
braces
glasses
dress alike

bookworm
quiet, serious
loves babies and animals
good at tennis

Read the Literature Link on Worktext page 292. Complete the Venn diagram with the information you read about Taiwan and America.

Taiwan

America

Amy's first letter to Dawn in *Peanut Butter Friends in a Chop Suey World* shows what she thinks and feels about the differences between Taiwan and America. List at least three of these thoughts or feelings with a partner.

_____

_____

_____

_____

_____

Parts of a Compare–Contrast Essay

A **compare-contrast essay** explains the similarities and differences between two people, places, or things.

The first paragraph, the introduction, tells what the essay is going to be about.

The second paragraph compares the two instruments, telling how they are alike.

The third paragraph contrasts the two instruments. It tells how they are different.

The fourth paragraph, the conclusion, sums up how the writer feels about both instruments.

The Piano and the Organ

At my church we have a piano and an organ. I have played on both of them a little bit. They look similar, but they have a lot of differences.

The piano and the organ have some likenesses. They both have keyboards with black and white keys. You play them both by pressing these keys to get different notes. They both also have pedals that change the volume. Both the piano and organ are often used in churches.

Pianos and organs have a lot in common, but they are very different instruments. Our church organ is a pipe organ. When you press its keys or pedals, air blows through pipes to make the sound. However, when you press piano keys, soft hammers strike metal strings. Our organ has three short keyboards, but our piano has only one long keyboard. The organ has stops that make it sound like many different types of instruments like trumpets or flutes. In contrast, the piano has only one type of sound. The organ has many pedals that play different notes. But our piano has only three pedals, and they do not play notes.

I'm glad my church has both a piano and an organ. I like the way both of them sound. Even though I am already taking piano lessons, I want to learn how to play the organ too.

Underline the topic sentence in each paragraph.

Read the compare-contrast essay. Label the parts of the essay.

A Comparing
B Contrasting
C Introduction
D Conclusion

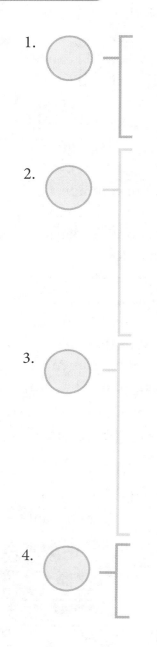

1.

2.

3.

4.

Math and English

We study several different subjects each day at school. Two of the subjects we are studying are math and English. We have noticed some similarities but also some differences between these two subjects.

Math and English are similar in some ways. We have both of these subjects in the morning after recess. Both of them have a story that we listen to at the beginning of a unit. We do worktext pages for both subjects. Similarly, we do writing for both subjects. In English, we write stories, poems, and essays. In math, our teacher has us keep a journal about what we are learning every week. We also use the computer for both subjects.

But there are many differences between math and English. In math we study numbers, but in English we study words and sentences. In math we sometimes get to use calculators, but we do not need those for English. Knowing math helps us when we are counting, buying something, or cutting a pizza. On the other hand, English helps us when we are reading books, writing letters, or giving oral reports in class.

We are glad God allows us to study both math and English. Some of us like one subject more than the other, but both subjects are interesting and important to learn.

Compare–Contrast Essay: Writing Together

Use a T-Chart and Venn diagram to plan an essay with your teacher.

| List details about two subjects on a T-Chart.

| Mark the details that are alike.

| Organize the details in a Venn diagram.

Math | English

Math	English
sometimes use calculator	study words and sentences
study numbers	do writing
do writing	story at the beginning of each unit
story at the beginning of each unit	helps with reading, writing, or giving reports
use computer	use computer
helps with counting, buying, or cutting a pizza	worktext page
worktext page	in the morning after recess
in the morning after recess	don't ever use calculator

Math   English

Math
sometimes use calculator
study numbers
helps with counting, buying, or cutting pizza

(shared)
do writing
story at beginning of each unit
use computer
worktext page
in the morning after recess

English
don't ever use calculator
study words and sentences
helps with reading, writing, or giving reports

Use the details from the Venn diagram to draft the essay.

Continued

Comparing and contrasting words will help connect the details in the essay.

Comparing Words	Contrasting Words
also	but
both	however
like	in contrast
similarly	even though
in the same way	on the other hand

Use proofreading marks to add comparing or contrasting words to make the paragraphs clearer.

England and Scotland are alike in many ways. They are part of the United Kingdom, and they are on the same island. People in England and Scotland speak English, and they use the same money system. England and Scotland have big cities and beautiful countrysides.

England and Scotland have some differences. England's official church is Anglican. Scotland's official church is Presbyterian. England is famous for the sport of cricket. Scotland is known for developing the game of golf. Some of the foods that are popular in England are different from the foods that Scottish people eat.

Proofreading Marks

∧∨	Add
ℯ	Delete
≡	Capital letter
/	Lowercase
⟳→	Move

Planning with a T-Chart

Begin to plan your essay by listing details about both subjects on a T-Chart.

Piano	Organ
black and white keys	three short keyboards
press keys to play	black and white keys
one long keyboard	press keys to play
hammers strike strings to make sound	many pedals
three pedals	air blows through pipes to make sound
pedal changes volume	pedals play notes
pedals don't play notes	pedal changes volume
one type of sound	used in churches
used in churches	stops make it play many sounds

Possible Ideas

1. Two of your aunts
2. A school morning and a Saturday morning
3. Two of your uncles
4. A bicycle and a motorcycle
5. Two kinds of fruit
6. Two animals
7. Two kinds of storms
8. Your front yard and your neighbor's front yard
9. Two museums you have visited
10. Two cities you have visited
11. Two holidays
12. Two kinds of art

What two things will you compare and contrast in your essay?

Remember to choose two people, places, or things that are different but have some things in common.

Write your two subjects as the headings on the T-Chart. List details about each subject on the chart. Remember to include both likenesses and differences.

Planning with a Venn Diagram

Continue to plan by marking the details that are similar on the T-Chart. Then complete the Venn diagram.

Piano	Organ
(black and white keys)	three short keyboards
(press keys to play)	(black and white keys)
one long keyboard	(press keys to play)
hammers strike strings to make sound	many pedals
three pedals	air blows through pipes to make sound
(pedal changes volume)	pedals play notes
pedals don't play notes	(pedal changes volume)
one type of sound	(used in churches)
(used in churches)	stops make it play many sounds

Use the Venn diagram to plan the paragraphs.

1 Introduction

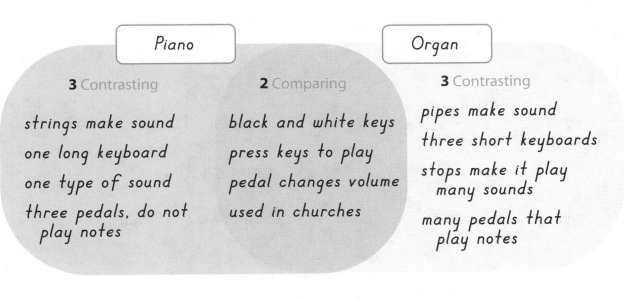

Piano		Organ
3 Contrasting	**2** Comparing	**3** Contrasting
strings make sound	black and white keys	pipes make sound
one long keyboard	press keys to play	three short keyboards
one type of sound	pedal changes volume	stops make it play many sounds
three pedals, do not play notes	used in churches	many pedals that play notes

4 Conclusion

Mark the details that are similar on your T-Chart on page 300. Then complete the Venn diagram. In each circle write the number for the part of the essay where the ideas will be used.

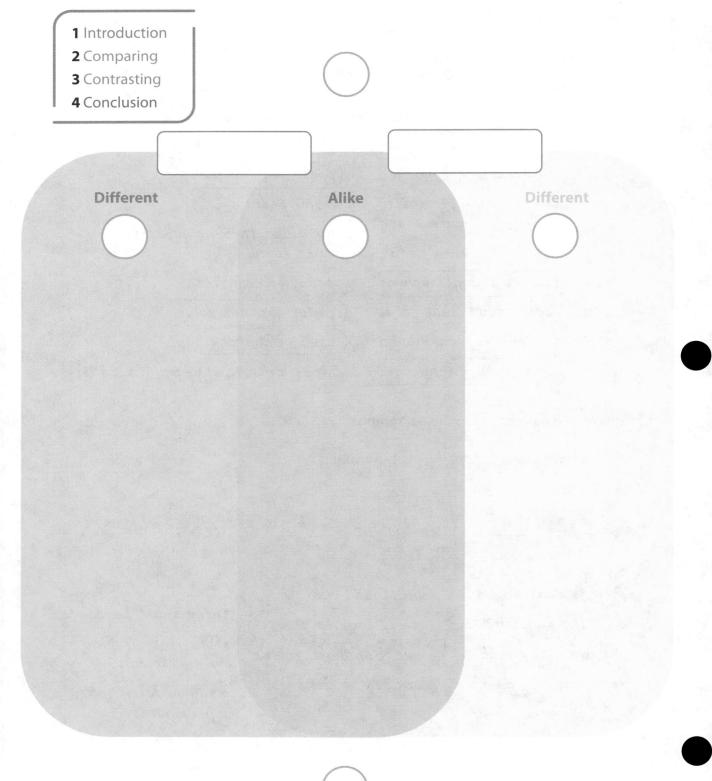

1 Introduction
2 Comparing
3 Contrasting
4 Conclusion

Different   Alike   Different

Compare-Contrast Essay: Draft

Draft your essay using the details from your Venn diagram. The essay you write should have four paragraphs: an introduction, a comparing paragraph, a contrasting paragraph, and a conclusion.

The Piano and the Organ

At my church we have a piano and an organ. I have played on both of them a little bit.

The piano and the organ have some likenesses. They are both at my church. They both have keyboards with black and white keys. You play them both by pressing these keys to get diffrent notes. They both also have pedals that change the volume. Both the piano and organ is often used in churches.

Pianos and organs are very diffrent instruments. Our church organ is a pipe organ. When you press it's keys or pedals, air blows through pipes to make the sound. When you press piano keys, soft hammers strike metal strings. Our organ has three short keyboards, but our piano has only one long keyboard. The organ has stops that make it sound like many different types of

Continued

instruments. The piano has only one type of sound. The organ has many pedals that play different notes. But our piano has only three pedals, and they do not play notes.

Im glad my church has both a piano and an organ. I like the way both of them sound. I am already taking piano lessons. I want to learn how to play the organ someday too.

Comparing Words	Contrasting Words
also	but
both	however
like	in contrast
similarly	even though
in the same way	on the other hand

Use the details from your Venn diagram to draft your compare-contrast essay. Use the drafting guide to check off the parts of the essay as you write. Remember to use comparing and contrasting words to connect details.

Drafting Guide	
Introduction	Tell about the two subjects you will be comparing and contrasting in the main part of the essay.
Comparing	Tell how the two subjects are alike.
Contrasting	Tell how the two subjects are different.
Conclusion	End by summing up the main part of the essay.

Compare-Contrast Essay: Revise

In a peer conference, writers can give and receive helpful ideas for revising their work.

| As you make suggestions, think about comments that have helped you. Speak as you would want someone to speak to you.

| Consider your peer's suggestions carefully.

An added sentence leads into the main part of the essay.

This detail has already been told in the introduction.

Contrasting words connect details in the third paragraph.

The Piano and the Organ

At my church we have a piano and an organ. I *They look similar but they have a lot of differences.* have played on both of them a little bit. ∧

The piano and the organ have some likenesses. ~~They are both at my church.~~ They both have keyboards with black and white keys. You play them both by pressing these keys to get diffrent notes. They both also have pedals that change the volume. Both the piano and organ is often used in churches.

have a lot in common, but they
Pianos and organs ∧ are very diffrent instruments. Our church organ is a pipe organ. When you press it's keys or pedals, air blows *However,* through pipes to make the sound. ∧ When you press piano keys, soft hammers strike metal strings. Our organ has three short keyboards, but our piano has

Continued

> only one long keyboard. The organ has stops that make it sound like many different types *like trumpets or flutes* of instruments. The piano has only one type of sound. The organ has many pedals that play different notes. But our piano has only three pedals, and they do not play notes.
>
> Im glad my church has both a piano and an organ. I like the way both of them sound. *Even though* I am already taking piano lessons, I want to learn how to play the organ someday too.

An added detail describes different sounds an organ can make.

The writer added contrasting words and then combined two sentences.

Use the revising checklist to help you revise your essay.

Revising Checklist
My essay compares two things.
My essay contrasts two things.
My introduction leads into the main part of the essay.
I included just enough details in the comparing paragraph—not too many and not too few.
I included just enough details in the contrasting paragraph—not too many and not too few.
I used comparing and contrasting words.
My conclusion sums up the main part of the essay.

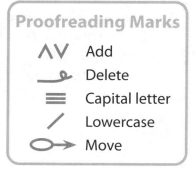

Proofreading Marks

∧∨ Add
↵ Delete
≡ Capital letter
/ Lowercase
⟳→ Move

Compare-Contrast Essay: Proofread

Proofread your essay to find and correct mistakes.

The Piano and the Organ

At my church we have a piano and an organ. I have played on both of them a little bit. They look similar ⌄ but they have a lot of differences.

The piano and the organ have some likenesses. They both have keyboards with black and white keys. You play them both by pressing these keys to get ~~diffrent~~ *different* notes. They both also have pedals that change the volume. Both the piano and organ ~~is~~ *are* often used in churches.

Pianos and organs have a lot in common, but they are very ~~different~~ *different* instruments. Our church organ is a pipe organ. When you press ~~it's~~ *its* keys or pedals, air blows through pipes to make the sound. However, when you press piano keys, soft hammers strike metal strings. Our organ has three short keyboards, but our piano has only

Continued

one long keyboard. The organ has stops that make it sound like many different types of instruments like trumpets or flutes. The piano has only one type of sound. The organ has many pedals that play different notes. But our piano has only three pedals, and they do not play notes.

Im glad my church has both a piano and an organ. I like the way both of them sound. Even though I am already taking piano lessons, I want to learn how to play the organ someday too.

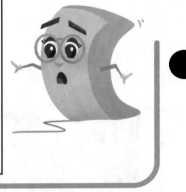

Use the proofreading checklist to help you proofread your essay.

Proofreading Checklist	
I indented each paragraph.	
I began each sentence with a capital letter and ended it with a punctuation mark.	
I used correct punctuation within sentences.	
I used correct verb forms.	
I used pronouns correctly.	
I corrected misspelled words.	

Proofreading Marks

∧∨ Add

✐ Delete

≡ Capital letter

/ Lowercase

⟳→ Move

Reflection

Two brothers wrote about the technology rules their parents have made for them. Complete the Venn diagram to compare and contrast the two descriptions.

Albert

Our parents have given us some rules for using our computer tablets. Sometimes I wish I could use my tablet longer or keep it in my room, but I know my parents are trying to help us build good habits. They want us to use our time wisely and use technology safely. Some people say my parents are too strict, but I know they love me and want the best for me.

Harold

Our parents made a bunch of technology rules and won't let us use our computer tablets much at all. I can't even store my tablet in my room. Dad says he and Mom are trying to keep us safe, but I think they are trying to keep us from having fun. If my parents really loved me, they would stop telling me what to do all the time.

Albert   Harold

Answer the questions about the two descriptions.

1. What makes the descriptions different?

_____

_____

_____

2. Which description do you like better? Explain your answer.

_____

_____

_____

_____

Cumulative Review

Read the paragraph and complete the activities.

> ①Mom and Grandma canned peaches today. ②Her washed, peeled, and sliced the peaches. ③Clean, shiny jars lined the Countertop. ④Mom put the peaches in the jars, and she twisted the jar lids on tight. ⑤Then Grandma place the jars in the kettle of hot water. ⑥I like fresh apples better than peaches. ⑦Soon a delightful peachy aroma filled the kitchen.

Read the sentence from the paragraph. Choose the best way to write the sentence or choose "No change."

1. Sentence 2
   - ○ You washed, peeled, and sliced the peaches.
   - ○ They washed, peeled, and sliced the peaches.
   - ○ No change

2. Sentence 3
   - ○ clean shiny jars lined the Countertop.
   - ○ Clean, shiny jars lined the countertop.
   - ○ No change

3. Sentence 4
   - ○ Mom put the peaches in the jars and she twisted the jar lids on tight.
   - ○ Mom put the peaches in the jars she twisted the jar lids on tight.
   - ○ No change

4. Sentence 5
   - ○ Then Grandma placing the jars in the kettle of hot water.
   - ○ Then Grandma placed the jars in the kettle of hot water.
   - ○ No change

Mark the sentence that does not belong in the paragraph.

5. ○ Sentence 5
   - ○ Sentence 6
   - ○ Sentence 7

Mark the best word to complete the sentence.

6. You will need to clean your room by ___ this afternoon.
   ○ you   ○ your   ○ yours   ○ yourself

7. The Haas family is coming to ___ house for supper.
   ○ we   ○ us   ○ our   ○ ours

8. ___ will enjoy the apple pie we are having for dessert.
   ○ They   ○ Them   ○ Theirs   ○ Themselves

9. Your sister made the pie by ___.
   ○ she   ○ herself   ○ her   ○ hers

10. They are coming to visit ___.
    ○ we   ○ ourselves   ○ them   ○ us

Mark the sentence with the adjective or adverb used correctly.

11. ○ The fastest land animal in the world is the cheetah.
    ○ The most fast land animal in the world is the cheetah.

12. ○ The Holstein cow is more popular than the Jersey cow.
    ○ The Holstein cow is the most popular than the Jersey cow.

13. ○ The brown chicken is the best egg layer of all my chickens.
    ○ The brown chicken is the better egg layer of all my chickens.

14. ○ A raccoon is the worse pet for an apartment.
    ○ A raccoon is the worst pet for an apartment.

15. ○ A male peacock is beautifuler than a female peacock.
    ○ A male peacock is more beautiful than a female peacock.

Identify the underlined words.

16. Since our friends in the green house moved, we have been lonely.
    ○ prepositional phrase   ○ independent clause   ○ dependent clause

17. Since our friends in the green house moved, we have been lonely.
    ○ prepositional phrase   ○ independent clause   ○ dependent clause

18. Since our friends in the green house moved, we have been lonely.
    ○ prepositional phrase   ○ independent clause   ○ dependent clause

Study and Research Skills

13

Who or what can guide me when I look for truth?

Brazil

Language Link

Facts about Brazil

KEY
- Cane Sugar
- Vanilla
- Coffee Beans
- Soy Beans
- Cinnamon
- Pepper

This country is home to many brightly colored animals, such as toucans, poison dart frogs, and jaguars.

hello!   ola!

Many Brazilian people are Catholic.

Brazil

is the largest country in South America. Although the official language for most countries in South America is Spanish, people in Brazil speak Portuguese. The most popular sport in the country is soccer. Brazil produces and exports coffee, soybeans, and sugar cane. Cinnamon, pepper, and vanilla can be made from plants that grow in the Amazon rainforest. Brazil was the first country in South America to host the Olympic games. Millions of tourists visit Brazil each year.

Rio de Janeiro

A statue called *Christ the Redeemer* is located in Rio de Janeiro. It is one of the seven wonders of the modern world.

Using the Library

Libraries are a valuable source of information. Fiction, nonfiction, and reference materials can all be found in different sections of a library.

Fiction books tell made-up stories. They are arranged in alphabetical order by the author's last name.

Nonfiction books contain facts about real people, places, animals, things, and events. They are arranged by subject and are assigned call numbers to help people locate the books quickly.

Reference books include dictionaries, encyclopedias, thesauruses, and atlases.

Biographies contain the life stories of real people and are arranged in alphabetical order by the last name of the person that the book is about.

A **library catalog** can help you find specific books. The catalog can be searched by title, author, subject, or keyword.

Mark the best way to search for the book described.

1. You know the author's name but don't know the title of the book.
   - ○ title
   - ○ author
   - ○ subject or keyword

2. You don't know the title of the book or the author's name.
   - ○ title
   - ○ author
   - ○ subject or keyword

3. You know the title of the book but don't know the author's name.
   - ○ title
   - ○ author
   - ○ subject or keyword

Match the description with the correct resource.

> **A** biography   **B** fiction   **C** nonfiction   **D** reference

_____ 4. A dictionary, encyclopedia, or thesaurus

_____ 5. A book that tells a make-believe story

_____ 6. A book that tells facts

_____ 7. A book that tells the life story of a real person

Write the best word or words for the library search. Then mark the best type of search to use.

8. A book by Ruth Martin about the way bananas grow

Search: [   ]

○ title   ○ author   ○ subject or keyword

9. A picture book called *Pedro's Little Sister*

Search: [   ]

○ title   ○ author   ○ subject or keyword

10. A book about the history and culture of Argentina

Search: [   ]

○ title   ○ author   ○ subject or keyword

11. A biography of Simón Bolivar

Search: [   ]

○ title   ○ author   ○ subject or keyword

Reference Books and Periodicals

Different kinds of reference books can help you find different types of information.

An atlas is a book of maps.

A dictionary gives definitions of words.

An encyclopedia is a set of books that contain articles about important people, places, inventions, animals, and events in history. Encyclopedia articles can be found in print books or online.

A periodical is a written work that is published at regular times during the year. Periodicals include magazines and newspapers.

Books have different parts to help you find information quickly.

The title page, copyright page, and table of contents are located in the front of a book.

The glossary and index are located in the back of a book.

Match the research question with the most helpful reference book.

A atlas   **B** dictionary   **C** encyclopedia   **D** periodical

_____ 1. How is the word *prepare* pronounced?

_____ 2. What kind of money is used in Argentina?

_____ 3. Who are the players on this year's Brazilian national soccer team?

_____ 4. How many inches of rainfall does Mexico get?

Mark the best answer.

5. Where would you look to find the page number where Chapter 3 begins?
   ○ index   ○ glossary   ○ table of contents

6. Where would you look in an English grammar book to find the page number for information about using commas?
   ○ index   ○ glossary   ○ table of contents

Match the research question with the most helpful reference book.

A atlas   B dictionary   C encyclopedia   D periodical

_____ 7. What is the name of the ocean that borders Brazil?

_____ 8. What events happened in my city last week?

_____ 9. What is the definition of the word *prescribe*?

_____ 10. Are there any interesting customs or holidays in Ecuador?

Mark the best answer.

11. Where would you look to find the name of the author of a book?
    ○ index   ○ glossary   ○ title page

12. Where would you look to find the meaning of a word found in a book?
    ○ index   ○ glossary   ○ table of contents

13. Where would you look to find the year that a book was published?
    ○ title page   ○ table of contents   ○ copyright page

Use a reference book or periodical to find the answer to one of the questions in numbers 7–10. Write down one or two sentences about the information that you find.

14. _____

_____

_____

_____

Bibliography Practice

A **bibliography** tells others where you found information. To make a bibliography, you will need to take notes about the research sources that you use.

Books, Magazines, Encyclopedias

Source ● book   ○ magazine   ○ encyclopedia

Author(s) _Amir Flores_

Title of article _____

Title of source _Exploring the Amazon_

Publisher _Traveler Press_   **For encyclopedia only**

Date of publication _2022_   Edition number _____

Page number(s) _____   Volume number _____

Source ○ book   ● magazine   ○ encyclopedia

Author(s) _Joseph Barnes_

Title of article _"Amazing Animals of the Amazon"_

Title of source _Science and More_

Publisher _____   **For encyclopedia only**

Date of publication _July 2021_   Edition number _____

Page number(s) _20-22_   Volume number _____

Continued

Books, Magazines, Encyclopedias

Source   ◯ book   ◯ magazine   ● encyclopedia

Author(s) _____

Title of article _"Suriname"_____

Title of source _The Travel Encyclopedia_____

Publisher _Wide World Press_____   **For encyclopedia only**

Date of publication _2020_____   Edition number _3_____

Page number(s) _312_____   Volume number _17_____

Internet source

Author(s) _Arianna Mitchell_____

Title of article _"All about Bananas"_____

Title of source (website) _Fun with Fruit_____

URL address _www.funwithfruit.net/bananas_____

Bibliography Practice

Use the form to write down the bibliography information for the sources that your teacher provides.

Books, Magazines, Encyclopedias

1. **Source**   ◯ book   ◯ magazine   ◯ encyclopedia

   Author(s) _____

   Title of article _____

   Title of source _____

   Publisher _____   **For encyclopedia only**

   Date of publication _____   Edition number _____

   Page number(s) _____   Volume number _____

2. **Source**   ◯ book   ◯ magazine   ◯ encyclopedia

   Author(s) _____

   Title of article _____

   Title of source _____

   Publisher _____   **For encyclopedia only**

   Date of publication _____   Edition number _____

   Page number(s) _____   Volume number _____

Internet Source

3. Author(s) _____

   Title of article _____

   Title of source (website) _____

   URL address _____

Use the form to write down the bibliography information for the sources that your teacher provides.

Books, Magazines, Encyclopedias

4. **Source** ○ book ○ magazine ○ encyclopedia

   Author(s) _____

   Title of article _____

   Title of source _____

   Publisher _____ **For encyclopedia only**

   Date of publication _____ Edition number _____

   Page number(s) _____ Volume number _____

5. **Source** ○ book ○ magazine ○ encyclopedia

   Author(s) _____

   Title of article _____

   Title of source _____

   Publisher _____ **For encyclopedia only**

   Date of publication _____ Edition number _____

   Page number(s) _____ Volume number _____

Internet Source

6. Author(s) _____

   Title of article _____

   Title of source (website) _____

   URL address _____

Internet Research

A **web browser** is a computer program that allows you to access the internet.

The **URL**, or web address, is the information at the top of a website that tells where the website can be found on the internet.

A **search engine** will help you find websites about topics that interest you.

A **keyword search** tells the search engine what kind of information you want to find.

Think of a keyword search that you could use to help you find the answer to the research question. Write your keywords in the blank.

1. What kinds of animals live in South America?

   Search:

2. Which country in South America is the smallest?

   Search:

3. What languages are spoken in South America?

   Search:

4. What is the capital of Peru?

   Search:

5. What kinds of foods do people in South America eat?

   Search:

Choose one of the questions from numbers 1–5. With help from an adult, go to a search engine and enter a keyword search using your keywords. Then complete numbers 6–8.

6. Look at the list of results from your keyword search. Was your search successful?

   ○ yes   ○ no

7. If you answered no, think of another keyword search. Write your new keyword or words in the blank.

   Search: _____

8. Try your new keyword search. Did you get better results?

   ○ yes   ○ no

Follow the link to one of the websites from your list of search results. Write down the bibliography information for that source.

Internet source

9.   Author(s) _____

     Title of article _____

     Title of source (website) _____

     URL address _____

Internet Safety

As you search for information, remember internet SAFETY.

S   Serve and love others with technology.

A   Avoid websites that you do not have permission to visit.

F   Focus on words that please God.

E   Evaluate what you read.

T   Tell an adult if you see something that makes you uncomfortable.

Y   Your passwords, address, and phone number should not be shared online.

Decide what you should do in each situation. Discuss your answers with a partner.

1. Someone you know is being bullied online.
2. You get a message asking for your address.
3. You see bad pictures on a website.
4. A person you have never met wants to be your friend online.
5. While you are doing research, you find a website with pop-ups that say "Click here!"

Write a sentence about a way that you could serve and love others with technology.

6. _____

_____

_____

A **reliable source** is trustworthy.

> To decide if a source is reliable, check the author, content, date, and website where you found the information.

> When you are looking for facts, check to make sure you can find at least two sources that say the same thing.

Read the source description. Write *R* if the source is reliable or *U* if the source is unreliable. If you decide the source is unreliable, mark the problem or problems that you find.

_____ 7. A report about Mexican tree frogs written by eight-year-old Josiah Hayes and posted on his class website

     ○ author   ○ content   ○ date   ○ website

_____ 8. A list of reasons why llamas make the best pets on BuyYourPetHere.com

     ○ author   ○ content   ○ date   ○ website

_____ 9. An article about Blue Morpho Butterflies by Professor James Martinez on the National Geographic website

     ○ author   ○ content   ○ date   ○ website

_____ 10. An article about the number of people who live in Peru posted on a government website on December 12th, 2005

     ○ author   ○ content   ○ date   ○ website

_____ 11. An article about the Amazon Rainforest called "Cutting Down Trees Should Be a Crime!" on TreesBeforePeople.blogz.com

     ○ author   ○ content   ○ date   ○ website

Taking Notes: Outlining

An **outline** is a way to organize information.

Outlines may be used in the planning stage of the writing process.

Outlines can also be used for taking notes on information that you hear or read.

Read the article about the Amazon River. Write the missing information in the outline.

The Great River of Brazil

The Amazon River is located in South America. It is the second longest river in the world. Only the Nile River is longer. The Amazon's muddy waters begin high in the Andes Mountains of Peru. Then the river flows across Brazil and eventually it surges into the Atlantic Ocean.

Many kinds of animals live in and around the Amazon River. A type of crocodile called the black caiman is the most dangerous animal in the water. Anaconda snakes dwell along the riverbanks. They can grow up to thirty feet long. Thousands of insects, including mosquitoes and water beetles, hover over the murky, brown water.

The Amazon River

I. Facts about the river

    A. _____

  ____. Second longest river in the world

  ____. Begins in Peru and flows to Atlantic Ocean

II. _____

    A. _____

    B. _____

    C. Mosquitoes and water beetles

Read the article about Bolivia. Write the missing information in the outline.

Bolivia

Bolivia is a great place to visit. Tourists can enjoy a variety of activities. Many tourists enjoy hiking or skiing in the beautiful mountains. Jungle tours allow people to see the rainforest from the comfort of a canoe. Fishing is a relaxing activity for tourists who are less active.

Bolivia's weather is usually mild. Temperatures vary greatly between day and night. The rainy season begins in November and ends in March.

Bolivia

I. Activities in Bolivia

_____. Hiking or skiing

    B. _____

    C. _____

II. _____

    A. Mild

_____. Temperatures change during the day

    C. _____

Taking Notes: Making a Note Card

Use a **note card** to help you collect information for a research report.

Note Card Guidelines

1. Summarize main ideas by stating them in your own words. Do not copy sentences.
2. Instead of complete sentences, write keywords and phrases to help you remember the information.
3. If you need to record the author's exact words, use quotation marks.
4. Take notes for only one main idea on each card.
5. Write the title of the book, article, or website and the page number at the bottom of the card.
6. Include the volume number with the page number for an encyclopedia. No page number is needed for a website.

Here is an excerpt from page three of an article called "Amazing Animals of the Amazon." Notice that each detail on the note card is about the main idea at the top of the card.

The River Dolphin

The Amazon river dolphin is also called the pink river dolphin. Although these animals are born gray, their skin turns pink as they grow up. They have long, narrow snouts lined with many teeth. Their flexible spines allow them to swim around branches and tree roots. Like the dolphins that live in the ocean, river dolphins can communicate by making beeping and whistling sounds.

River Dolphin

1. pink
2. long noses
3. lots of teeth
4. flexible bodies

"Amazing Animals of the Amazon," p. 3

Read the following excerpt from a website called *Fun with Fruit*. Take notes on the card to help you remember the details. Write the information about the source.

All about Bananas

The hot and humid climate of Brazil makes it a good place to grow bananas. These bright yellow fruits have many health benefits. They are full of potassium and vitamin B6. The banana plants look like trees but are actually herbs. Bananas grow in bunches with about ten to twenty bananas in each. Men use machetes to harvest the bananas before they ripen.

Facts about Bananas

1. _____

2. _____

3. _____

4. _____

Read the following encyclopedia article taken from page 312 of *The Travel Encyclopedia*, Volume 17. Take notes to help you remember the details. Write the information about the source.

Suriname

Suriname is a very small country located on the northern coast of South America. Most of the people live near the coast because of the thick jungles. Most of the roads in this country are also located near the coast. A lot of the jungles are only accessible by airplane or by boat. Many unusual animals, such as the sloth, the giant armadillo, the jaguar, and the ocelot, live in this country.

Facts about Suriname

1. _____

2. _____

3. _____

4. _____

Practice

Read the article about Brazil. Write the missing information in the outline.

Brazilian Coffee Production

Brazil is one of the largest coffee producers in the world. Many Brazilian people are employed in the coffee industry. The coffee plant is grown on large plantations. These coffee farms grow over 40 million bags of coffee a year. The southeast area of Brazil grows the most coffee. The whole country benefits from coffee production. Coffee is an important product grown in Brazil.

The coffee bean is actually a seed produced by a coffee plant. The coffee plant or tree produces a cherry-like fruit that can be yellow, red, or orange when ripe. The fruit is harvested, dried, and milled. The beans are roasted and bagged on these large coffee farms. The production of coffee takes three to four months. The bags of coffee beans are shipped to countries all over the world. One-third of the world's coffee comes from Brazil.

Brazilian Coffee Production

I. Brazilian coffee producers

    A. _____

    ____. Coffee is grown on farms

    ____. _____

II. _____

    A. The seed of a coffee plant

    ____. _____

    C. Coffee is shipped all over the world

Read the following excerpt from a website called *Brazilian Lifestyle*. Take notes on the card to help you remember the details. Write the information about the source.

Coffee Customers

In Brazil coffee is a favorite drink of people of all ages. More people drink coffee in Brazil than almost any other country in the world. Brazil's finest coffee is shipped to other countries, but the coffee that is not shipped is sold cheaply at coffee shops and restaurants. Brazilians like black coffee, and many drink it with sugar. The government of Brazil encourages everyone to drink coffee, even children. Children often drink coffee with milk. Milky coffee is a delicious delight for children. Brazilians are proud of their coffee product. Almost everyone in Brazil is a coffee customer.

Facts about Coffee
1. _____
2. _____
3. _____

Chapter 13 Review

Write the best word or words for the library search. Then mark the best type of search to use.

1. A biography of Christopher Columbus

Search: [   ]

   ○ title   ○ author   ○ subject or keyword

2. A book called *One Hundred Spanish Words*

Search: [   ]

   ○ title   ○ author   ○ subject or keyword

3. A travel book by Jackson Roberts

Search: [   ]

   ○ title   ○ author   ○ subject or keyword

Match the research question with the most helpful reference book.

A atlas   **B** dictionary   **C** encyclopedia   **D** periodical

_____ 4. How many syllables are in the word *preparation*?

_____ 5. Which types of parrots can learn to talk?

_____ 6. What is the name of the longest river in South America?

_____ 7. Who won last week's election?

Think of a keyword search that you could use to find the answer to the research question. Write your keywords in the blank.

8. Who was Amerigo Vespucci?

Search: [   ]

9. Is the Galapagos tortoise endangered?

Search: [   ]

Read the source description. Write *R* if the source is reliable or *U* if the source is unreliable. If you decide the source is unreliable, mark the problem or problems that you find.

_____ 10. An article about a two-headed alpaca on FishyFactz.com

○ author ○ content ○ date ○ website

_____ 11. An article about plants in the Amazon rainforest posted by a scientist from Brazil

○ author ○ content ○ date ○ website

Read the article about llamas. Write the missing information in the outline.

The Lively Llama

Llamas live in South America. A llama's wool is usually white or brown. A baby llama is called a cria. Because they do not like to be alone, llamas usually live in herds.

These friendly animals are very useful to humans. Their wool is soft and warm. Llamas can be trained and are often used as pack animals. Some ranchers use llamas to guard flocks of sheep.

Llamas

I. Characteristics

____. Live in South America

B. _____

C. _____

II. _____

A. Soft, warm wool

____. Good pack animals

C. _____

Read the following article from a website called *Travel the World*. Take notes to help you remember the details. Write the information about the source.

The Mountains of South America

The world's longest mountain range is called the Andes. These mountains stretch across Argentina, Chile, Ecuador, Peru, Bolivia, Venezuela, and Colombia. Some of the mountains are volcanoes. Ecuador has the world's tallest active volcano. The Andes Mountains are full of minerals like iron, copper, silver, and gold.

The Andes Mountains

1. _____

2. _____

3. _____

Journal

Research is hard work. We serve others well when we present information that is accurate and well researched.

Write down the research question that you have chosen.

1. _____

_____

Research your question and write down the answer.

2. _____

_____

_____

_____

Present your research question and the information that you found to another person.

Cumulative Review

1. Princess is my cat.

2. The mouse jumped up.

3. Princess caught the mouse.

4. Princess played with the fuzzy mouse.

● 5. The little mouse is gray.

6. The mouse fell under the sofa.

7. The black cat chased it.

8. The gray mouse is a fun toy.

●

Mark the sentence that is written correctly.

9. ○ Jared's trumpet case is heaviest than my case.
   ○ Jared's trumpet case is heavier than my case.

10. ○ I clean my instrument most often than Jared.
    ○ I clean my instrument more often than Jared.

11. ○ Emma played well this morning.
    ○ Emma played good this morning.

12. ○ No one could have done it gooder.
    ○ No one could have done it better.

Mark the word that best completes the sentence.

13. Ashlynn plays soccer with ___ sister.
    ○ their   ○ her   ○ she

14. The two girls practice ___ drills every day.
    ○ her   ○ them   ○ their

15. Mikaela punts to Ashlynn because ___ is the goalie.
    ○ she   ○ her   ○ they

16. ___ are the most dedicated players on the team.
    ○ She   ○ Them   ○ They

Identify the underlined words.

17. When school ended, children enthusiastically cheered in the halls of our school.
    ○ prepositional phrase   ○ independent clause   ○ dependent clause

18. When school ended, children enthusiastically cheered in the halls of our school.
    ○ prepositional phrase   ○ independent clause   ○ dependent clause

19. When school ended, children enthusiastically cheered in the halls of our school.
    ○ prepositional phrase   ○ independent clause   ○ dependent clause

20. When school ended, children enthusiastically cheered in the halls of our school.
    ○ prepositional phrase   ○ independent clause   ○ dependent clause

Writing a Research Report

What kinds of details are important in research?

Language Link

Fun Facts about Switzerland

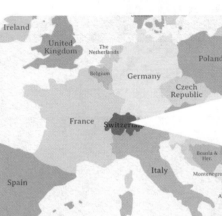

Switzerland

Switzerland has four national languages: French, German, Italian, and Romansch.

Many famous people from world and church history lived in Switzerland.

Alpenhorn playing is a beloved musical tradition in Switzerland.

The pine marten and the Alpine ibex live in Switzerland.

Tourists can stroll through an ice palace that has been carved inside a glacier.

The country is well known for cheese making, banking, and watch making.

St. Bernard dogs are famous for their past rescues of lost mountain travelers.

Switzerland's different climates support glaciers in the mountains, farms on the plateau, and palm trees in the South.

Dufourspitze is the highest mountain peak in Switzerland.

The Swiss invented milk chocolate.

TOBLERONE

Choosing a Research Topic

A **research report** gives facts about a topic. Your opinions, or how you feel about the topic, are not included.

| **Research** is gathering facts from nonfiction sources. Before you write, research carefully to serve your readers well.

Steps for Writing a Good Research Report

1. Choose your topic.
2. Decide what main ideas you want to write about.
3. Read and take notes about your main ideas from nonfiction sources.
4. Organize your information by writing an outline.
5. Write the first draft of your report from the outline.
6. Revise your report.
7. Proofread your report.
8. Make a list of all the sources you used in your report.
9. Publish your report.

Write the names of two places you might be interested in learning more about.

_____   _____

Write the name of the place you have chosen and complete the chart.

> Which place would you enjoy learning more about?

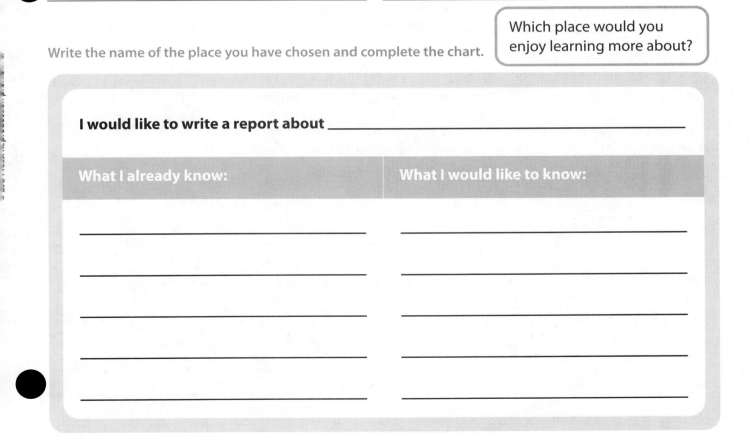

I would like to write a report about _____

What I already know:	What I would like to know:
_____	_____
_____	_____
_____	_____
_____	_____
_____	_____

Mark the statement that describes the best research choice.

1. Travis is choosing a topic for his research report. He should _____.
   - ○ choose Canada because he knows a lot about Canada already
   - ○ choose Mexico because two of his friends plan to write about Mexico
   - ○ choose South Korea because he has always wanted to learn more about the country where his grandparents were born

2. Riley found a book on her topic that she liked better than any other source she found. She should _____.
   - ○ take all of her notes from that book because it is so much more interesting than any of the others
   - ○ take notes from several sources to use ideas from different authors
   - ○ copy her favorite paragraph to use as the first paragraph of her report

3. Megan wonders if a detail she found in an online article about Egypt is really a fact. She should _____.
   - ○ decide that the detail must be accurate since she found it on the internet
   - ○ ask her best friend at recess whether the detail sounds true or not
   - ○ see if she can find the same detail about Egypt in three reliable sources

4. Waylan returned one of his books to the library and noticed later that he had not written down the author's name. He should _____.
   - ○ use the title search on the online library catalog to find the information about the book he needs
   - ○ make up a name to save time
   - ○ decide that no one will really need the author's name anyway

Select a good research choice from numbers 1–4. Discuss it with a partner. Write one or two sentences describing how the choice could help a reader of the report.

5. _____

_____

_____

_____

_____

_____

Parts of a Research Report

Research reports use paragraphs to tell about the topic.

The introduction is the first sentence of the report. It tells where the place is.

A topic sentence begins each paragraph and tells one main idea. The other sentences in the paragraph give details about the main idea in the topic sentence.

The conclusion is a sentence that sums up your topic.

Underline the parts of the research report. Use the colors green, blue, orange, and red.

Seeing Switzerland

Switzerland is a small country in Europe. It is about half the size of South Carolina. This country has many mountains. The Jura Mountains lie on the northwest border, and the Swiss Alps tower in the southern and eastern parts of the country. The Swiss Plateau sits between the two ranges. Many lakes and rivers provide water and electric power.

Switzerland has different climates. For example, some mountains stay snowy all year, but the Swiss Plateau has a milder climate. Palm trees grow in warmer places farther south. Total rainfall can be from 45 to 100 inches each year.

There is much to see and do in Switzerland. Travelers enjoy the land, scenery, and traditions. They ski, hike, or ride boats and trains. Tourists also taste Swiss chocolate and cheese. Shoppers can buy well-crafted watches made by skilled watchmakers. Visitors see traditional villages and festivals. They watch Swiss wrestling and stone-putting. They also learn about history at museums, famous churches, and monuments.

The national flag shows some of Switzerland's history. In 1339 Swiss soldiers began wearing the white cross as a symbol of Christianity. Switzerland's flag has a white cross sitting in the middle of a square red field. The Red Cross was founded much later by a Swiss man, and its flag is much like Switzerland's. There is much to discover about the small country of Switzerland.

Research Report

Introduction

Topic Sentence

Details

Conclusion

Write the main idea of each paragraph in the model research report.

   I. _____

  II. _____

 III. _____

 IV. _____

Write the four main ideas that you will research about the place you have chosen.

   I. _____

  II. _____

 III. _____

 IV. _____

Research Report: Taking Notes

Take notes using the four main ideas about your topic. Each main idea will be one paragraph in your research report.

> Write each main idea at the top of a separate note card.

> Make new note cards as you find more details about each main idea.

Use at least two sources. Record full information about each source in a separate place for the **bibliography**, a list of the sources of information used to write the report.

I. Switzerland's Geography
II. Switzerland's Climate
III. Things to See and Do in Switzerland
IV. Switzerland's Flag

Switzerland is on the continent of Europe. Its landscape is varied. The Alps stand guard to the south and east. The Jura Mountains line Switzerland's northwest boundary. The rugged peaks of the Alps stretch higher than the Jura. The Jura also have a more rounded appearance. Across the middle of the country is the Swiss Plateau. This area is also called the Mittelland (German for "middle land"). Switzerland is landlocked, but it has an abundant water supply from numerous lakes and rivers. The country produces large amounts of hydroelectric power. The extra power is used by nearby nations.

Switzerland's Geography

1. Alps in the south and east (taller than the Jura Mountains)
2. Jura Mountains along northwest border
3. Swiss Plateau between ranges (also called Mittelland)
4. Many lakes and rivers provide water, electric power

Everyone's Encyclopedia, p. 90

How to Take Notes

- Write facts.
- Write only enough words to remember the information.
- Do not copy sentences.

Mark the correct answer.

1. The title at the top of each note card should be _____.
   - ○ the name of the topic you will be researching
   - ○ one main idea about the topic you will be researching

2. When taking notes from a book, it is a good idea to _____.
   - ○ copy exactly what the author said to use in your report
   - ○ write down just enough to remember the information

3. When you are finished with your research, you should have completed _____.
   - ○ several note cards about each of the main ideas you researched
   - ○ only one note card about each main idea you researched

4. After taking notes from a source, you should always _____.
   - ○ write information about the source
   - ○ write only the author's name at the bottom of the card

5. The list of all the sources you used to write your report is called a _____.
   - ○ biography
   - ○ bibliography

Write the answer to the question.

6. What are two possible sources you could look in to find information for your report?

   _____

7. What are the four main ideas you will research for your report? (Include the name of the place you have chosen.)

   I. _____

   II. _____

   III. _____

   IV. _____

Begin locating and reading information about the place of your choice. As you read, take notes on separate note cards. Record information about the source at the bottom of each note card.

Research Report: Writing an Outline

Organize your information in an **outline**.

Use your four main ideas as the four main points of your outline.

Identify each main point with a Roman numeral.

List the most important details from your note cards under each main point.

Things to See and Do in Switzerland

1. Skiing (downhill and cross-country), hiking, biking, train and boat rides
2. Traditional villages, festivals
3. Museums, churches, monuments

"Sights of Switzerland" in <u>Travel Europe</u>, page 16

Things to See and Do in Switzerland

1. Famous for cheese, chocolate, skilled watch making
2. Unusual traditional sports—stone putting (throw 184-pound stone), schwingen (Swiss wrestling)
3. St. Bernard dog rescued lost travelers, Swiss hound (a hunting dog)

<u>The Big Book of Switzerland</u>, page 43

III. Things to See and Do in Switzerland
   A. Enjoy scenery—ski, bike, hike, ride boats and trains
   B. Look at things made in Switzerland—taste chocolate, cheese; buy a watch
   C. Explore traditions—visit villages and festivals, watch unusual sports
   D. Learn about history—museums, churches, monuments

Compare the note cards to the outline. Mark the correct answer.

1. How many details did the writer list altogether on these two note cards?
   ○ 3   ○ 5   ○ 6

2. How many of the details on these note cards did the writer use in the outline?
   ○ 4   ○ 5   ○ 6

Read the two note cards about Switzerland's geography. Choose the four details that you believe are the most important and write them in outline form.

Switzerland's Geography

1. Alps in the south and east (taller than the Jura Mountains)
2. Jura Mountains along northwest border
3. Swiss Plateau between ranges (also called Mittelland)
4. Many lakes and rivers provide water, electric power

Everyone's Encyclopedia, p. 90

Switzerland's Geography

1. In Europe; half the size of South Carolina
2. Alps and Jura Mountains on either side of Swiss Plateau
3. Rhine and Rhone important rivers; sources of both are in Switzerland
4. Many fossils in the Jura Mountains

"A Trip through Switzerland" www .swisstravels.com/atripthroughswitzerland

I. Switzerland's Geography

A. _____

_____

B. _____

_____

C. _____

_____

D. _____

_____

Write an outline to organize the information from your note cards for writing your research report. Choose the most important facts to include in your outline. Each main idea should have at least three supporting details.

Research Report: Draft

Draft your research report using the main ideas and details in your outline.

> I. Switzerland's Geography
>   A. Small European country half the size of South Carolina
>   B. Mountain ranges: Jura Mountains, Alps
>   C. Swiss Plateau between the two ranges
>   D. Many rivers and lakes provide water and electric power
> II. Switzerland's Climate
>   A. Some mountains snowy all year
>   B. Milder climate on the Swiss Plateau
>   C. Palm trees in warm southern parts of country
>   D. Yearly rainfall 45 to 100 inches

Swiss Plateau

Switzerland

Switzerland is a small country. It is about half the size of south Carolina. This country has many mountains. The Jura Mountains lies on the northwest border, and the Swiss Alps tower in the southern and eastern parts of the country. I would like to climb the Matterhorn someday. The Swiss Plateau sits between the two ranges. Many lakes and rivers give water and electric power.

Continued

Switzerland has different climates. Some mountains stay snowy all year. The Swiss Plateau has a milder climate. Palm trees grow in warmer places farther south. Total rainfall can be from 45 to 100 inches each year.

Draft your research report using your outline. Use the drafting guide to check off the parts of the report as you write.

Drafting Guide	
Introductory Sentence	Tell where the place is.
Details	Give details about the first main idea.
Topic Sentence	Write a topic sentence about the second main idea.
Details	Give details about the second main idea.
Topic Sentence	Write a topic sentence about the third main idea.
Details	Give details about the third main idea.
Topic Sentence	Write a topic sentence about the fourth main idea.
Details	Give details about the fourth main idea.
Concluding Sentence	End your report with a sentence about the place.

Research Report: Revise

Revise your research report. Write down questions and comments from your peer conference to help you make improvements.

1. Your report tells interesting facts about Switzerland and makes me want to find out more!
2. Did you want to tell where Switzerland is?
3. Your opinion about climbing the Matterhorn should not be included in a research report.

> An added word makes the title more interesting.

Seeing Switzerland
      ^

> The introduction now tells where the place is.

Switzerland is a small country. It is about
                                    in Europe
                                         ^
half the size of south Carolina. This country has

many mountains. The Jura Mountains lies on the

northwest border, and the Swiss Alps tower in

the southern and eastern parts of the country. ~~I~~

> A research report should give facts, not opinions.

~~would like to climb the Matterhorn~~ someday. The

Swiss Plateau sits between the two ranges. Many

> The writer used the thesaurus to find a more exact word.

                    provide
lakes and rivers ~~give~~ water and electric power.
                   ^
                              For example,
Switzerland has different climates. ~~S~~ome

> Transition words connect ideas.

                        year, but the
mountains stay snowy all ~~year. The~~ Swiss Plateau
                                 ^

> Combined sentences add more variety.

has a milder climate. Palm trees grow in warmer

places farther south. Total rainfall can be from

45 to 100 inches each year.

Read your report with a partner. Write any questions or comments your partner has about the information in your report.

1. _____

_____

2. _____

_____

3. _____

_____

Take time to read your outline and look through your note cards again if you need to search for additional details.

Use the revising checklist to help you revise your report. Try to include answers to your partner's questions.

Revising Checklist	
My introduction tells where the place is.	
Each paragraph is about one main idea.	
All of the sentences in each paragraph tell about its main idea.	
I included enough details.	
All of my sentences tell facts.	
I used exact words.	
My conclusion sums up my topic.	

Proofreading Marks

∧∨	Add
ℯ	Delete
≡	Capital letter
/	Lowercase
⟳	Move

Research Report: Proofread

Proofread your research report to find and correct mistakes. Read the report several times to check for each item on the proofreading checklist.

Seeing Switzerland

Switzerland is a small country in Europe. It is about half the size of ~~south~~ Carolina. This country has many mountains. The Jura Mountains

lie
~~lies~~ on the northwest border, and the Swiss Alps tower in the southern and eastern parts of the country. The Swiss Plateau sits between the two ranges. Many lakes and rivers provide water and electric power.

Switzerland has different climates. For example, some mountains stay snowy all year, but the Swiss Plateau has a milder climate. Palm trees grow in warmer places farther south. Total rainfall can be from 45 to 100 inches each year.

There
~~Their~~ is much to see and do in Switzerland. Travelers enjoy the land, scenery, and traditions. They ski hike or ride boats and trains. Tourists also taste Swiss chocolate and cheese. Shoppers can buy well-crafted watches made by skilled watchmakers. Visitors see traditional villages

Continued

and festivals. They watch Swiss wrestling and stone-putting. They also learn about history at museums, famous churches, and ~~monuements~~ ^*monuments*^.

The national flag shows some of Switzerland's history. In 1339 Swiss soldiers began wearing the white cross as a symbol of Christianity. Switzerland's flag has a white cross sitting in the middle of a square red field. The Red Cross was founded much later by a Swiss man, and ~~it's~~ ^*its*^ flag is much like Switzerland's. There is much to discover about the small country of Switzerland.

Use the proofreading checklist to help you proofread your report.

Proofreading Checklist
I began each sentence with a capital letter and ended it with a punctuation mark.
I used correct capitalization within sentences.
I used correct punctuation within sentences.
I used correct verb forms.
I used pronouns correctly.
I corrected misspelled words.

Proofreading Marks

∧∨ Add

⟋ Delete

≡ Capital letter

／ Lowercase

⟜⟶ Move

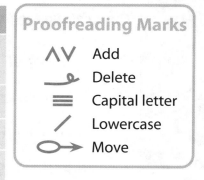

The Bibliography

A **bibliography** is a list of all the sources you used in your report. This list may include books, encyclopedias, magazine articles, or internet sources.

The bibliography tells others where you found the information and gives proper credit to the authors.

A bibliography lists the sources in alphabetical order by the authors' last names.

Bibliography

Burri, Tristan. <u>The Big Book of Switzerland</u>. Agar Press, 2019.

Hess, Elias. "Switzerland." <u>Everyone's Encyclopedia</u>, 4th ed., vol. 7, Taylor Children's Press, 2021, p. 90.

Studer, Trina. "Sights of Switzerland." <u>Travel Europe</u>, April 2022, pp. 16-18.

Sutter, Selina. "A Trip through Switzerland." <u>Swiss Travels</u>, www.swisstravels.com /atripthroughswitzerland.

The bibliography lists all the information needed for locating each source.

Basic format for a book:

Last name, First name of author. <u>Title of Book</u>. Publisher, year of publication.

Basic format for an internet article:

Last name, First name of author. "Title of Article." <u>Name of Website</u>, URL.

See Bibliographic Form on Handbook pages 382–83.

© BJU Press. Reproduction prohibited.

Chapter 14: Writing a Research Report | Lesson 177

Books, Magazines, Encyclopedias

Source   ● book   ○ magazine   ○ encyclopedia

Author(s) _Peter Robiero_

Title of article _____

Title of source _Visiting Italy_

Publisher _Vineyard Press_   **For encyclopedia only**

Date of publication _2022_   Edition number _____

Page number(s) _____   Volume number _____

Source   ○ book   ○ magazine   ● encyclopedia

Author(s) _Erma Neigh_

Title of article _"Italy"_

Title of source _The Travel Encyclopedia_

Publisher _World Press_   **For encyclopedia only**

Date of publication _2021_   Edition number _4_

Page number(s) _133_   Volume number _8_

Internet Source

Author(s) _Leo Walley_

Title of article _"Modern Italian Customs"_

Title of source (website) _Your World_

URL address _www.yourworld.org/modernitaliancustoms_

Write a bibliography using the information above. See Bibliographic Form on Handbook pages 382–83 for the proper form.

_____

_____

_____

_____

Write the bibliography for your report. List the sources alphabetically by the authors' last names and use the proper form.

Reflection

You and your friend Rex are talking after soccer practice. He brags, "My older brother wrote this really cool research report ten years ago. I'm going to copy most of it into my report. It's okay because the teacher won't recognize it—she didn't even live in our state when my brother was in our grade. I can even copy most of his note cards and his bibliography too. That's just the same as finding stuff in books or online. The teacher said we can't copy our report from books or online articles, but I'm not doing that. I'll get a good grade because my brother's really smart, and it'll be lots easier than doing all the research myself."

How could you answer Rex? Write a note to Rex explaining why his plan is wrong.

_____

_____

_____

_____

_____

Cumulative Review

Read the sentence. Place parentheses around any prepositional phrase. Then diagram the sentence.

1. Jesus loved the people.

———————————————|——————————————————

2. The crowd was hungry.

———————————————|——————————————————

3. The boy gave two small fish.

———————————————|——————————————————

4. The people sat on the grass.

———————————————|——————————————————

5. Jesus offered thanks to God.

———————————————|——————————————————

6. Twelve disciples handed bread to the people.

———————————————|——————————————————

7. Jesus performed a great miracle.

———————————————|——————————————————

8. Jesus is the Prophet.

———————————————|——————————————————

Mark the sentence that is written correctly.

9. ○ People is the most important part of God's creation.
   ○ The Bible tells us that people are made in God's image.
   ○ That make people very special to God.

10. ○ The sun is the largest object in our solar system.
    ○ The moon is closest to Earth than the sun.
    ○ Venus is the most bright planet in our solar system.

11. ○ The brightest star in our solar system.
    ○ Can be observed in the night sky in the winter.
    ○ People have been studying stars since Bible times.

Mark the best way to combine the sentences.

12. Tornados produce strong swirling winds.
    Hurricanes produce strong swirling winds.
    ○ Tornados produce strong swirling winds, hurricanes produce strong winds, too.
    ○ Tornados and hurricanes produce strong swirling winds.

13. Blizzards are snowstorms with strong winds.
    Blizzards are snowstorms with freezing temperatures.
    ○ Blizzards are snowstorms with strong winds and freezing temperatures.
    ○ Blizzards are snowstorms with strong winds and blizzards have freezing temperatures.

Mark whether the underlined clause is dependent or independent.

14. I want to visit all of the national parks <u>when I am older</u>.
    ○ dependent clause   ○ independent clause

15. <u>Since California has national parks with giant sequoias</u>, I will go there first.
    ○ dependent clause   ○ independent clause

16. Because I enjoy exploring <u>I will also tour the Mammoth Cave</u>.
    ○ dependent clause   ○ independent clause

17. <u>Hawaii has a national park</u> where there is an active volcano.
    ○ dependent clause   ○ independent clause

18. The tour of the national parks will not be complete <u>until I see the Grand Canyon</u>.
    ○ dependent clause   ○ independent clause

Handbook

Thesaurus

A *thesaurus* contains a list of synonyms, words that have similar meanings. A thesaurus helps the writer find exact, interesting, unusual, and appropriate words.

- The *entry words* are arranged in alphabetical order.
- *Guidewords* can help you locate a word.
- Each entry gives a *definition* and uses the word in a *sample sentence*.
- A list of *synonyms* that can be used to replace the entry word is provided.
- The entry also tells the *part of speech*, how the word is used in the sentence.
- Some entries include an *antonym*, a word that has the opposite meaning of the entry word.

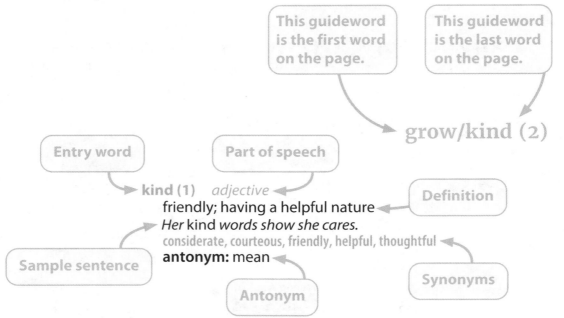

This guideword is the first word on the page.

This guideword is the last word on the page.

grow/kind (2)

Entry word

Part of speech

kind (1) *adjective*

Definition

friendly; having a helpful nature

Her kind *words show she cares.*

considerate, courteous, friendly, helpful, thoughtful

antonym: mean

Sample sentence

Synonyms

Antonym

The following sentence tells the reader what the person's words are like. Changing the word *kind* will give a more precise meaning to each sentence. When choosing a synonym, be careful not to change the meaning of the sentence.

> *Her* kind *words show she cares.*
>
> *Her* considerate *words show she cares.*
> *Her* courteous *words show she cares.*
> *Her* friendly *words show she cares.*
> *Her* helpful *words show she cares.*
> *Her* thoughtful *words show she cares.*

afraid *adjective*
filled with fear
He is afraid *of the dark.*
fearful, frightened, nervous, scared, uneasy, worried
antonym: confident

angry *adjective*
showing strong feeling that comes from believing one has been treated badly
She was angry *with him for reading her diary.*
aggravated, annoyed, enraged, fuming, furious, irate, offended, resentful, wrathful
antonym: calm

answer *noun*
a spoken or written reply to a question, statement, invitation, or letter
She knows the answer *to the question.*
reply, response
antonym: question

ask *verb*
to put a question to; to invite an answer to
Ask the librarian for help.
inquire, interrogate, petition, question, request
antonym: answer

attack *verb*
to set upon with force or violence
The armies attack *the city.*
afflict, assault, harm, invade, raid
antonym: defend

bad *adjective*
not as it should be; of poor quality
His spelling is bad.
awful, dreadful, horrible, horrid, hurtful, rotten, terrible
antonym: good

before *adverb*
earlier; sooner
I read that book before.
already, earlier, previously, prior to
antonym: after

beg *verb*
to ask for humbly or earnestly
The man begged *for forgiveness.*
ask, demand, entreat, plead
antonyms: demand, urge

big *adjective*
of great size, number, or amount
A redwood is a big *tree.*
enormous, gigantic, grand, great, huge, large, massive
antonym: little

bother *verb*
to annoy; to disturb
Please do not bother *your sister.*
annoy, disturb, harass, interrupt, irritate, pester, provoke
antonym: comfort

brave *adjective*
having or showing courage
The brave *man rescued the boy from the cave.*
bold, confident, courageous, daring, heroic, valiant
antonym: cowardly

break *verb*
to cause to separate into parts
Break the cookie in half.
crack, crush, damage, fracture, separate, shatter, smash, wreck
antonym: repair

bright *adjective*
giving off much light; brilliant in color
A lone star twinkled faintly above the bright *city lights.*
brilliant, illuminating, luminous, radiant, shining, vivid
antonym: dull

build *verb*
to make or form by joining parts or materials together; to construct
Let's build *a fence.*
construct, form, shape
antonym: destroy

buy *verb*
to get goods or services for a payment
We will buy *fruit at the store.*
obtain, purchase
antonym: sell

calm *adjective*
quiet; still; peaceful
The wind became calm *after the storm.*
peaceful, placid, serene, still, tranquil, undisturbed
antonyms: excited, angry, troubled

careful *adjective*
watchful; trying to avoid danger or harm
They are careful *when crossing the street.*
cautious, prudent, vigilant, watchful
antonym: careless

carry *verb*
to move or take from one place to another
The men carry *furniture into the house.*
haul, lug, move, tote, transport

change *verb*
to make or become different
The student changed *his answer to the question.*
alter, replace, shift, substitute, switch, transform, vary
antonym: remain

clean (1) *adjective*
free from dirt, stain, or germs
The kitchen floor is clean.
immaculate, neat, pure, sanitary, spotless, stainless, tidy
antonyms: soiled, dirty

clean (2) *verb*
to get rid of dirt, stain, or germs
You should clean *a wound to prevent infection.*
cleanse, disinfect, purify, sanitize, wash
antonym: soil

cold *adjective*
having a low temperature
Today the weather is snowy and cold.
chilly, cool, frigid, frosty, frozen, icy
antonym: hot

collect *verb*
to come or bring together in a group
The girls collect *stickers.*
accumulate, compile, gather, obtain, reserve, store
antonym: scatter

copy *verb*
to make to be like or look like something else
Please copy *this report.*
duplicate, replicate, reproduce

cry *verb*
to shed tears because of a feeling of pain or sorrow
I sometimes cry *when I am hurt.*
bawl, mourn, sob, wail, weep, whimper
antonym: laugh

cut *verb*
to separate into pieces with a sharp-edged tool
Mom cut *the apple with a knife.*
chop, dice, gash, rip, shred, slice, snip, tear

dangerous *adjective*
threatening harm or injury; unsafe
The weatherman described the dangerous *winds of the hurricane.*
hazardous, perilous, risky
antonym: safe

dark *adjective*
having little or no light
No moon rose on that dark *night.*
cloudy, dim, dull, overcast
antonym: light

destroy *verb*
to completely ruin or break into pieces
The tornado destroyed *many buildings.*
annihilate, demolish, devastate, ruin, wreck
antonym: make

different *adjective*
unlike; not the same
A frog is different *from a toad.*
distinct, unique, unlike, unusual
antonyms: same, alike

dirty *adjective*
unclean; not pure
My shirt was dirty *after I played with the dog.*
filthy, grimy, muddy, nasty, polluted, soiled
antonym: clean

disappear *verb*
to pass from sight
The chocolate cookies always disappear *first.*
fade, vanish
antonym: appear

do *verb*
to perform or carry out
What will you do *this summer?*
achieve, complete, perform, practice, undertake

easy *adjective*
needing little effort or thought
This book is easy *to read.*
effortless, simple, uncomplicated
antonym: difficult

empty *adjective*
containing nothing; not occupied
The house was empty *when we left.*
deserted, unoccupied, vacant, void
antonym: full

enough *adjective*
as much or as many as needed
I earned enough *money for a new bike.*
adequate, plenty, sufficient
antonym: insufficient

fair *adjective*
just; honest
The judge made a fair *decision.*
consistent, honest, impartial, just, lawful, legal, right
antonym: unfair

fake *adjective*
false; not genuine
The criminal tried to spend fake *money.*
artificial, counterfeit, false, fraudulent, phony
antonym: real

fat *adjective*
having a great amount of fat; plump
That is a very fat *cat.*
bulky, chubby, enormous, large, massive, obese
antonym: thin

fear *noun*
a strong feeling that danger may be near
She has a fear *of dogs.*
alarm, dismay, dread, fright, terror

find *verb*
to come upon; to discover by searching
Did you find *my keys?*
discover, encounter, locate, recover
antonym: lose

finish *verb*
to come to the end of
Did you finish *your science project?*
accomplish, complete, conclude, terminate
antonyms: start, begin

fix *verb*
to make stable; to repair
Could you fix *the broken faucet?*
mend, repair, restore
antonym: break

funny *adjective*
causing laughter; humorous
The funny *joke made us laugh.*
amusing, comical, hilarious, humorous
antonym: serious

get *verb*
to receive; to come to have
Will we get *a puppy?*
acquire, gain, obtain, receive
antonym: give

give *verb*
to hand over or present to someone
We give *money to the missionaries.*
contribute, donate, grant, offer, present, provide, supply
antonyms: get, receive

gloomy *adjective*
a state of mind or atmosphere that is dark or discouraging
The day was gloomy *because of the dark clouds.*
bleak, depressing, dismal, dreary, somber
antonym: cheerful

go *verb*
to move or travel to a place
We go *to Washington State every year.*
depart, leave, move, proceed, race, run, travel
antonyms: stay, remain

good (1) *adjective*
high in quality
He used a good *map for the trip.*
favorable, helpful, right, suitable, superb, terrific, useful, wonderful
antonym: bad

good (2) *adjective*
pleasing; agreeable
The cookies are good *to eat.*
delightful, enjoyable, fabulous, pleasant
antonym: bad

great *adjective*
remarkable; very skillful
George Washington was a great *leader.*
awesome, excellent, exceptional, fantastic, grand, important, magnificent, outstanding, wonderful
antonyms: terrible, awful

group   *noun*
a number of persons or things together
The state of Hawaii is made up of a group *of islands in the Pacific Ocean.*
clump, cluster, collection, bunch, gathering, set, team
antonym: individual

grow   *verb*
to increase in size
The trees grow *every year.*
develop, increase, mature
antonym: shrink

guard   *verb*
to keep safe; to protect
Two big dogs guard *the house.*
defend, keep, protect, shield, watch

happy   *adjective*
cheerful; showing pleasure
The happy *children played and sang.*
carefree, cheerful, content, glad, joyful, jubilant, satisfied
antonym: sad

hard   *adjective*
difficult to do; requiring great effort
A police officer has a hard *job to do.*
complicated, difficult, tough, trying
antonym: easy

hate   *verb*
to dislike greatly
I hate *asparagus.*
abhor, despise, detest, dislike, loathe
antonym: love

hide   *verb*
to put out of sight
I will hide *Mom's gift.*
conceal, cover
antonym: show

high   *adjective*
extending far upward or being at a great height
Only Dad can reach that high *shelf.*
elevated, towering
antonym: low

hit   *verb*
to strike a blow
He hit *the nail with a hammer.*
pound, smack, smite, strike

hold   *verb*
to grasp with the arms or hands
Hold *the rope tightly.*
clasp, clutch, grasp, grip
antonym: release

honest   *adjective*
truthful; trustworthy
The honest *boy would not lie.*
respectable, sincere, trustworthy, upright
antonym: deceitful

hot   *adjective*
having a high temperature
The bread bakes in a hot *oven.*
burning, fiery, scorching, sweltering
antonym: cold

hurry   *verb*
to move or act with haste
Hurry *to get your shoes on!*
accelerate, hustle, rush

hurt   *verb*
to cause pain or harm
The boy fell and hurt *his knee.*
damage, harm, impair, injure, wound
antonym: help

important   *adjective*
having significant value or meaning
He had an important *message to give the president.*
impressive, influential, meaningful, momentous, significant, valuable
antonym: unimportant

job   *noun*
a chore, usually done on a regular schedule; an occupation
My job *is to feed the cat every day.*
career, chore, duty, employment, livelihood, profession, task, trade, work

join   *verb*
to put or bring together
He joined *the pieces of the puzzle.*
attach, combine, connect, fasten, link
antonym: disconnect

jump   *verb*
to use the legs to spring from the ground
Our cat jumps *from the ground to the porch.*
bounce, bound, hop, leap, spring up

kind (1)   *adjective*
   friendly; having a helpful nature
   Her kind *words show she cares.*
   considerate, courteous, friendly, helpful, thoughtful
   antonym: mean

kind (2)   *noun*
   a group of things that are the same in some way
   Lions and tigers are the same kind *of animal.*
   category, group, sort, type

laugh   *verb*
   to express joy or amusement with sounds and movements
   I always laugh *at Grandpa's funny stories.*
   chuckle, giggle, snicker
   antonym: cry

let   *verb*
   to permit; to allow
   My brother let *me bat first.*
   allow, consent, permit
   antonym: forbid

lift   *verb*
   to move from a lower to a higher position
   She will lift *the box.*
   elevate, hoist, raise
   antonym: lower

like   *verb*
   to enjoy; to find pleasing
   Our family likes *to camp in a tent.*
   enjoy, favor, prefer
   antonym: dislike

little   *adjective*
   small in size or amount
   Our little *table seats only three people.*
   miniature, minute, petite, short, tiny
   antonym: big

live   *verb*
   to make one's home
   I live *in a brick house.*
   abide, dwell, inhabit, occupy, reside

look (1)   *verb*
   to use one's eyesight
   Look *at the beautiful sunset.*
   behold, gaze, glance, observe, peer, stare, view, watch

look (2)   *verb*
   to search
   Look *everywhere for the kitten.*
   check, hunt, investigate, search, seek, survey

make   *verb*
   to cause to exist or happen
   I will make *a gift for you.*
   build, construct, create, form, mold, produce, shape
   antonym: destroy

many   *adjective*
   consisting of a large number; not few
   He has many *friends.*
   countless, multiple, numerous
   antonym: few

move   *verb*
   to change position or location; to go in a certain direction
   My grandparents will move *to Ohio.*
   budge, relocate, scoot, shift, transfer, transport

neat   *adjective*
   clean; tidy; orderly
   He has a neat *desk.*
   orderly, organized, tidy
   antonym: messy

needed   *adjective*
   necessary
   We don't have the needed *tools to fix the car.*
   essential, necessary, required
   antonym: unnecessary

new   *adjective*
   not existing or made until recently
   Don't walk on the new *grass.*
   fresh, immature, recent
   antonym: old

nice   *adjective*
   pleasant
   The weather is nice *and sunny today.*
   fine, good, kind, pleasant, pleasing
   antonyms: nasty, mean

noise   *noun*
   any sound, especially a sound that is loud, unpleasant, or unwanted
   We can hear the noise *of the traffic.*
   clamor, commotion, racket, sound, uproar

old   *adjective*

having lived for many years; made long ago

They visited a very old *castle.*

aged, ancient, elderly

antonym: young

part   *noun*

a section or piece of a whole

The bottom part *of the garage door is missing.*

section, segment, piece, portion

antonym: whole

perfect   *adjective*

without fault or flaw

Joe threw a perfect *pitch across the plate.*

accurate, faultless, flawless, precise

antonym: defective

pick   *verb*

to decide on or prefer something

She will pick *a leader.*

choose, decide, elect, select

antonym: overlook

polite   *adjective*

showing careful thought for others

We are polite *to the store workers.*

courteous, gracious, mannerly, tactful

antonym: impolite

pretty   *adjective*

delightful to look at, listen to, or think about

That is a pretty *painting.*

beautiful, gorgeous, lovely, marvelous, pleasing, wonderful

antonym: ugly

promise   *verb*

to give one's word to do or not to do something

I promise *to obey.*

agree, commit, declare, guarantee, pledge, vow

protect   *verb*

to keep from injury or damage; to guard

The firefighter's clothing protects *him from the fire.*

guard, preserve, shield

antonym: attack

proud (1)   *adjective*

overly satisfied with oneself

The proud *boy bragged about his family's money.*

arrogant, conceited, haughty, vain

antonym: humble

proud (2)   *adjective*

feeling very pleased or satisfied over something accomplished or owned

I am proud *of the A I got on my test.*

pleased, satisfied, fulfilled, contented, delighted, ecstatic, excited

antonym: ashamed

pull   *verb*

to use force to move something toward oneself

Pull the rope harder.

drag, jerk, tow, tug

antonym: push

push   *verb*

to press against in order to move

He tried to push *the rock into the hole.*

press, shove, thrust

antonym: pull

put   *verb*

to set in a certain place or position

Put the towels in the closet.

establish, install, lay, place, set

antonym: remove

quick   *adjective*

speedy; done in a short time

Mom made a quick *trip to the grocery store.*

fast, rapid, speedy, swift

antonym: slow

quiet   *adjective*

having little or no noise or activity

A farm is quiet *in the early morning hours.*

calm, hushed, peaceful, restful, silent, still, tranquil

antonym: noisy

real   *adjective*

genuine; not artificial

Real gems sparkled in his crown.

actual, authentic, genuine

antonym: fake

reason   *noun*

explanation or cause

What is his reason *for going to church?*

cause, goal, intention, motive, purpose

antonym: result

reliable *adjective*
able to be depended upon
She is a reliable *worker and will complete the job.*
dependable, faithful, responsible, trustworthy
antonym: unreliable

replace *verb*
to fill or take the place of
Replace *the silk roses with real roses.*
exchange, substitute, supersede, supplant, switch

rich *adjective*
having great or abundant wealth
The rich *man used his money to help others.*
affluent, prosperous, wealthy
antonym: poor

right *adjective*
correct; appropriate or proper
She wrote the right *answer to the question.*
accurate, correct, exact, proper, true
antonym: wrong

rough (1) *adjective*
having a surface that is uneven or not smooth
Our truck bounced over the rough *road.*
bumpy, coarse, jagged, rugged, uneven
antonym: smooth

rough (2) *adjective*
difficult, unpleasant, or challenging
He had a rough *day.*
difficult, severe, tough, trying, burdensome

run *verb*
to move quickly using the legs, not touching the ground with both or all feet at the same time
The soccer players run *after the ball.*
canter, dash, gallop, jog, race, sprint
antonym: walk

sad *adjective*
feeling or showing sorrow or unhappiness
He was sad *when it was time to leave.*
depressed, gloomy, sorrowful, unhappy
antonym: happy

same *adjective*
just like or identical to something else
My friend and I have the same *shoes.*
equivalent, identical
antonym: different

save *verb*
to keep for use in the future; to store up
It is wise to save *money.*
conserve, reserve
antonym: spend

say *verb*
to speak words aloud
Can you say *that more clearly?*
communicate, declare, exclaim, express, remark, speak, state, utter

scary *adjective*
causing alarm; frightening
Scary *stories keep me awake at night.*
alarming, fearful, frightening, horrifying, terrifying
antonym: pleasant

serious *adjective*
acting or looking thoughtful or grave
Dad looked serious *when he heard about the accident.*
earnest, grave, grim, somber, solemn
antonym: funny

shake *verb*
to move quickly up and down or back and forth
I felt my house shake *during the earthquake.*
quiver, rock, tremble, vibrate

shiny *adjective*
reflecting light; bright
Mother has a shiny *jewel in her ring.*
bright, brilliant, glistening, radiant
antonym: dull

short (1) *adjective*
happening for a brief time
I'm going for a short *walk.*
abrupt, brief, condensed, quick
antonym: long

short (2) *adjective*
having little length or height; low
The rope is too short.
miniature, tiny
antonym: long

shout *verb*
to call or cry out loudly
Don't shout *in the library.*
cheer, holler, scream, shriek, yell
antonym: whisper

show   *verb*
> to cause to be seen
> *Please* show *your science project to the judge.*
> demonstrate, display, exhibit, present, reveal
> **antonym:** hide

smart   *adjective*
> intelligent; having an alert mind
> *The* smart *doctor helped me get well.*
> bright, clever, ingenious, intelligent, shrewd, skillful
> **antonym:** unintelligent

smell   *noun*
> the sense by which odors are recognized; an odor or scent
> *I love the* smell *of pine trees.*
> aroma, fragrance, odor, stench, stink

smile   *verb*
> to show happiness, amusement, pleasure, or friendliness by an expression on the face
> *The teacher* smiled *kindly at the new student.*
> beam, grin
> **antonym:** frown

some   *adjective*
> an unknown or unnamed number or quantity
> *I have* some *baseball cards.*
> several, few, many

special   *adjective*
> different from what is common or usual
> *She uses* special *tools to make her crafts.*
> exceptional, extraordinary, particular, unusual
> **antonym:** ordinary

start   *verb*
> to begin a movement or activity
> *The game will* start *after lunch.*
> begin, commence, embark, initiate
> **antonym:** finish

stop   *verb*
> to cease a movement or activity
> *The driver* stopped *at the red light.*
> break, cease, halt, pause
> **antonyms:** begin, go

strange   *adjective*
> not known before; not familiar
> *Their dog has a* strange *name.*
> bizarre, different, odd, peculiar, unfamiliar, unusual, weird
> **antonym:** ordinary

strict   *adjective*
> firm or severe
> *Our principal is* strict *about silence during fire drills.*
> firm, grave, severe, stern
> **antonyms:** flexible, lenient

strong   *adjective*
> having much physical power
> *The* strong *elephant lifted the tree trunk.*
> fortified, great, mighty, muscular, powerful, sturdy
> **antonym:** weak

sure   *adjective*
> feeling certain, confident; having no doubt
> *I'm* sure *he will be at school.*
> certain, confident, positive
> **antonym:** uncertain

surprise   *verb*
> to cause to feel wonder at something unexpected
> *I will* surprise *my mother on her birthday.*
> amaze, astonish, shock, startle

take   *verb*
> to get or seize
> Take *a book from the shelf.*
> grab, grasp, seize, snatch, sneak, steal
> **antonym:** give

teach   *verb*
> to show how; to instruct
> *I'll* teach *you how to play the game.*
> direct, educate, guide, inform, instruct, show, train
> **antonym:** learn

thin   *adjective*
> skinny; not thick
> *That board is too* thin *for our project.*
> gaunt, lean, scrawny, slender, slight, slim
> **antonym:** thick

think   *verb*
> to use the mind
> Think *before you act.*
> consider, contemplate, imagine, meditate, muse, ponder, reflect

throw   *verb*

to cause to move through the air with a forward motion of the arm

Throw *the ball to Lance.*

cast, fling, hurl, pitch, toss

antonym: catch

tie   *verb*

to bind together or fasten with a cord, rope, or something similar

Let's tie *the twigs together with string.*

bind, fasten, hold, secure, wrap

antonyms: loosen, untie

tired   *adjective*

having lost strength or energy

Emma was tired *after raking the leaves.*

exhausted, fatigued, sluggish, weary

antonym: alert

travel   *verb*

to make a journey; to go from one place to another

He will travel *across the country.*

journey, sojourn, tour

trip   *noun*

a journey

Dad packed the car for our trip *to the mountains.*

excursion, journey, vacation, voyage

trouble   *noun*

a difficult situation; a need

The flood caused trouble *for the family.*

affliction, danger, difficulty, distress, grief, misery

antonym: safety

ugly   *adjective*

not pleasing to the eye; unsightly

We finally got rid of the ugly *brown carpet.*

gross, grotesque, hideous, homely, repulsive, unattractive

antonyms: beautiful, pretty

understand   *verb*

to get the meaning of

Now I understand *what this word means.*

comprehend, discern, grasp, know

antonym: confuse

usual   *adjective*

commonly used; ordinary

I ate my usual *breakfast.*

customary, expected, normal, ordinary, regular, typical

antonym: unusual

very   *adverb*

in a high degree

That part of the lake is very *deep.*

absolutely, extremely, fully, genuinely, truly

antonym: slightly

walk   *verb*

to go on foot

Let's walk *through the woods.*

amble, march, plod, saunter, step, stroll, strut, trudge

antonym: run

want   *verb*

to have a desire for

I want *to play outside.*

crave, desire, wish

waste   *verb*

to spend or use up carelessly or without valuable result

Don't waste *so much time playing video games.*

misspend, squander

antonym: save

weak   *adjective*

without strength or energy

He was weak *after his illness.*

feeble, frail, powerless

antonym: strong

wet   *adjective*

full of moisture

The wet *towels soon dried in the sun.*

damp, drenched, humid, saturated, soaked, soggy

antonym: dry

whole   *adjective*

complete; including all parts

They ate the whole *cake.*

complete, entire, total, undivided

antonym: part

work   *noun*

that which is done to accomplish something or to earn money

He has almost finished his work *in the yard.*

chore, duty, effort, employment, job, labor, livelihood, occupation, profession, task, toil, trade

antonym: play

worker   *noun*

one that works

She is a diligent worker.

employee, laborer

In a sentence, the **verb** tells what the subject does or is.

An **action verb** tells what the subject does.

Spot barked at the neighbors.

A **linking verb** tells what the subject is by connecting the subject to a noun or an adjective in the complete predicate.

Bubbles is my betta fish.

A **helping verb** helps the <u>main verb</u> in the sentence. Helping verbs come before the main verb.

My cat is <u>sleeping</u> in the sunshine.

Helping Verbs				
am	be	had	will	must
is	being	do	would	can
are	been	does	should	could
was	have	did	may	
were	has	shall	might	

Forms of the **verb** *be* can be linking verbs or helping verbs.

Forms of Be			
am	is	are	was
were	be	being	been

Sensory verbs can be action verbs or linking verbs.

Sensory Verbs				
look	taste	feel	smell	sound

Prepositions

A **preposition** shows the relationship between a noun or pronoun and the other words in a sentence.

The noun or pronoun that comes after the preposition is called the **object of the preposition**.

Bubbles swims around the tank. My cat watches him through the glass.

Common Prepositions		
about	beside	on
above	by	out
across	down	outside
after	for	over
along	from	through
around	in	to
at	inside	under
before	near	until
behind	of	up
below	off	with

Capitalizing Proper Nouns

1. Capitalize the names, initials, and titles of people.

   Doctor Castillo   Samantha L. Smith   Grandma

2. Capitalize the names and titles of God.

   Father   Holy Spirit   Son of God   Shepherd

3. Capitalize the names of buildings.

   Empire State Building   Grandville Courthouse

   Civic Hall   Lakeville Public Library

4. Capitalize the names of streets, cities, states, countries, rivers, lakes, and oceans.

   Ghana, West Africa   Atlantic Ocean   Drake Drive

   Missouri River   Lake Michigan   Phoenix, Arizona

5. Capitalize the names of specific days of the week, months, and holidays.

   Friday   September   Christmas

6. Capitalize the names of teams, businesses, and organizations.

   Parkview Panthers   Sam's Quickmart   Congress

7. Capitalize names of languages.

   Chinese   English   French

Capitalizing Titles

1. **Capitalize the first, last, and all important words in the titles of books, newspapers, magazines, stories, poems, and songs.**

   Silent **R**oad to **R**escue   *The Daily Times*   **T**aste of **H**ome

   "**J**ohnny and **H**is **M**ule"   "**W**ind on the **H**ill"   "**T**here **I**s a **F**ountain"

2. **Book, newspaper, and magazine titles should be underlined when handwritten or put in italics when typed on a computer.**

   Medallion   *Iceland Adventure*   Albia News   *Answers Magazine*

3. **Use quotation marks around the titles of stories, poems, and songs.**

   (story) "The Rich Man and Lazarus"   (poem) "Frost"

   (story) "The Legend of John Henry"   (song) "All Things Bright and Beautiful"

4. **Capitalize names of the Bible, its divisions, and its books.**

   God's **W**ord   **H**oly **B**ible   **N**ew **T**estament   **R**omans 8:28

Abbreviations

United States Postal Abbreviations

The United States Postal Service gives abbreviations for states and territories as two capital letters with no periods.

Alabama	**AL**	Montana	**MT**
Alaska	**AK**	Nebraska	**NE**
American Samoa	**AS**	Nevada	**NV**
Arizona	**AZ**	New Hampshire	**NH**
Arkansas	**AR**	New Jersey	**NJ**
California	**CA**	New Mexico	**NM**
Colorado	**CO**	New York	**NY**
Connecticut	**CT**	North Carolina	**NC**
Delaware	**DE**	North Dakota	**ND**
District of Columbia	**DC**	Northern Mariana Islands	**MP**
Florida	**FL**	Ohio	**OH**
Georgia	**GA**	Oklahoma	**OK**
Guam	**GU**	Oregon	**OR**
Hawaii	**HI**	Pennsylvania	**PA**
Idaho	**ID**	Puerto Rico	**PR**
Illinois	**IL**	Rhode Island	**RI**
Indiana	**IN**	South Carolina	**SC**
Iowa	**IA**	South Dakota	**SD**
Kansas	**KS**	Tennessee	**TN**
Kentucky	**KY**	Texas	**TX**
Louisiana	**LA**	Utah	**UT**
Maine	**ME**	Vermont	**VT**
Maryland	**MD**	Virgin Islands	**VI**
Massachusetts	**MA**	Virginia	**VA**
Michigan	**MI**	Washington	**WA**
Minnesota	**MN**	West Virginia	**WV**
Mississippi	**MS**	Wisconsin	**WI**
Missouri	**MO**	Wyoming	**WY**

Abbreviations

Days of the Week

Sunday	**Sun.**
Monday	**Mon.**
Tuesday	**Tues.**
Wednesday	**Wed.**
Thursday	**Thurs.**
Friday	**Fri.**
Saturday	**Sat.**

Titles of People

Titles are special words used with people's names. The names and titles of people are capitalized. Abbreviations are used for most titles. The title **Miss** does not have an abbreviation.

Mr. Flynn **(an adult man)**

Mrs. Chow **(an adult married woman)**

Ms. Green **(an adult woman)**

Miss Smith **(an unmarried woman)**

Dr. Joseph Brady **(a doctor)**

Rev. James McGraw **(an ordained preacher)**

Pres. Abraham Lincoln **(president)**

Sen. Mark Thompson **(senator)**

Gov. John Wood **(governor)**

Prof. Maria Diaz **(professor)**

Capt. Miles Bennett **(captain)**

Months of the Year

January	**Jan.**
February	**Feb.**
March	**Mar.**
April	**Apr.**
August	**Aug.**
September	**Sept.**
October	**Oct.**
November	**Nov.**
December	**Dec.**

May, **June**, and **July** have no abbreviations because they are short words.

Addresses

Apartment	**Apt.**	Drive	**Dr.**
Avenue	**Ave.**	Lane	**Ln.**
Boulevard	**Blvd.**	Post Office	**PO**
Circle	**Cir.**	Road	**Rd.**
Court	**Ct.**	Street	**St.**

Irregular Verbs

Verbs that do not add -ed when changed to the past tense are called **irregular verbs**.

Verb	Present Tense	Past Tense	Verb with *has, have, or had*
begin	begin, begins	began	begun
bring	bring, brings	brought	brought
come	come, comes	came	came
do	do, does	did	done
drive	drive, drives	drove	driven
eat	eat, eats	ate	eaten
fall	fall, falls	fell	fallen
fly	fly, flies	flew	flown
give	give, gives	gave	given
go	go, goes	went	gone
grow	grow, grows	grew	grown
make	make, makes	made	made
ride	ride, rides	rode	ridden
run	run, runs	ran	run
say	say, says	said	said
see	see, sees	saw	seen
sing	sing, sings	sang	sung
swim	swim, swims	swam	swum
take	take, takes	took	taken
tell	tell, tells	told	told
throw	throw, throws	threw	thrown
wear	wear, wears	wore	worn
write	write, writes	wrote	written

Homophones

Homophones are words that sound alike but have different meanings and usually different spellings.

ate	past tense of eat	We *ate* hot dogs for lunch.
eight	a number; 8	I found *eight* coins.
bill	money	I have a dollar *bill*.
bill	statement of money owed	The company sent me a *bill*.
bill	beak	The duck had an orange *bill*.
blew	action of the wind	The wind *blew* the door shut.
blue	a color	She wore a *blue* skirt.
can	to be able to	I *can* play the flute.
can	metal container	I opened a *can* of soup.
dear	loved or respected	A *dear* friend gave me a gift.
deer	an animal	We saw *deer* in the forest.
fair	honest	A good referee is *fair*.
fair	a carnival	Did you go to the *fair*?
fare	toll	The taxi *fare* was expensive.
file	collection of papers	Put the document in the *file*.
file	a tool for smoothing	I used the *file* for my nails.
flour	processed grain	Add *flour* to the dough.
flower	colorful plant petals	This *flower* is a daisy.
for	purpose	Mom made a cake *for* the party.
four	a number; 4	I wrote *four* sentences.
hair	grows on the head	Andy has red *hair*.
hare	rabbit	The *hare* hopped away.
heal	cure	My cut will *heal* itself quickly.
heel	bottom of the foot	My *heel* is sore.
hear	understand by listening	Can you *hear* him talking?
here	in this place	Please sit *here*.
him	a masculine pronoun	I sat next to *him*.
hymn	a song to God	We sang my favorite *hymn*.
hoarse	husky-voiced	He was *hoarse* from yelling.
horse	an animal	The cowboy rode a *horse*.
hole	tear, opening	There is a *hole* in my jacket.
whole	entire	We ate the *whole* pizza.

Continued

Homophones

its	possessive form of it	Return the book to *its* shelf.
it's	contraction of *it is*	I think *it's* going to rain.
knew	was aware of	I *knew* the answer.
new	just made or bought	Mike has *new* shoes.
knot	a twist or tangle	My shoelaces are in a *knot*.
not	negation of a word	I will *not* forget my lunch.
knows	is aware of	He *knows* about the surprise.
nose	organ of smelling	My *nose* is stuffy.
lock	a curl of hair	A *lock* of hair fell over her eyes.
lock	a fastener	Dad put a *lock* on the door.
might	power	Our God is a God of *might*.
might	will possibly happen	We *might* have to cancel the game.
mint	plant with fresh flavor	You can crush *mint* leaves to make a tea.
mint	place where coins are made	We visited the Denver *Mint*.
pair	couple; two things	I bought a *pair* of shoes.
pare	cut or peel	Will you *pare* the apples?
pear	juicy, grainy fruit	The *pear* was delicious.
plain	ordinary; nothing added	Grandpa wore a *plain* red tie.
plane	airplane	We flew on a *plane*.
rest	sleep	Did you get enough *rest*?
rest	the remainder	The *rest* of us will wait here.
right	the opposite of *left*	My house is on the *right*.
right	correct	He gave the *right* answer.
write	make letters or words	Please *write* neatly.
sea	body of water	The *sea* was still and blue.
see	to look	I *see* birds flying.
sent	past tense of *send*	I *sent* the letter to him.
cent	penny	The groceries cost seven dollars and one *cent*.
scent	a smell	Hunting dogs can track their prey by *scent*.

Homophones

shed	a building	Put the shovel in the *shed*.
shed	to take off	Snakes *shed* their skin.
stair	a step	The toddler sat on the *stair*.
stare	to gaze steadfastly	It is not polite to *stare*.
tail	body part attached to the back of an animal	The puppy wagged his *tail*.
tale	a story	"Paul Bunyan" is a tall *tale*.
their	possessive form of *they*	I'm going to *their* house.
there	at that place	Look over *there*.
they're	contraction of *they are*	*They're* coming with us.
to	direction of or toward	We drove *to* Washington.
too	also	I can play the piano *too*.
too	very	You worked *too* quickly.
two	a number; 2	He has *two* cookies.
way	path or direction	Which *way* should we go?
way	habit of doing things	That is the *way* we do it.
weigh	to measure the heaviness of something	I will *weigh* the apples.
weak	lacking strength	He was *weak* from hunger.
week	seven days	We spent a *week* at the beach.
well	a deep hole	She carried a bucket of water from the *well*.
well	correctly	You did *well* on the spelling test.
wood	part of a tree	Dad cut the *wood*.
would	past tense of *will*	He said we *would* go today.
your	possessive form of *you*	*Your* ice cream is melting.
you're	contraction of *you are*	*You're* invited to the party.

Bibliographic Form

A **bibliography** is a list of all the sources you used in your report. This list may include books, encyclopedias, magazine articles, or internet sources.

The bibliography tells others where you found the information and gives proper credit to the authors.

Bibliography

Burri, Tristan. <u>The Big Book of Switzerland</u>. Agar Press, 2019.

Hess, Elias. "Switzerland." <u>Everyone's Encyclopedia</u>, 4th ed., vol. 7, Taylor Children's Press, 2021, p. 90.

Studer, Trina. "Sights of Switzerland." <u>Travel Europe</u>, April 2022, pp. 16–18.

Sutter, Selina. "A Trip through Switzerland." <u>Swiss Travels</u>, www.swisstravels.com/atripthroughswitzerland.

A bibliography lists the sources in alphabetical order by the authors' last names.

The bibliography lists all the information needed for locating each source.

Bibliographic Form

Basic format for a book

Last name, First name of author. <u>Title of Book</u>. Publisher, year of
    publication.

    Burri, Tristan. <u>*The Big Book of Switzerland*</u>*. Agar Press, 2019.*

Basic format for an encyclopedia

Last name, First name of author. "Title of Article." <u>Title of</u>
    <u>Encyclopedia</u>, edition number, volume number, Publisher,
    year of publication, page numbers of article.

    Hess, Elias. "Switzerland." <u>*Everyone's Encyclopedia*</u>*, 4th ed., vol. 7,*
    Taylor Children's Press, 2021, p. 90.

Basic format for a magazine article

Last name, First name of author. "Title of Article." <u>Title of</u>
    <u>Magazine</u>, Date of publication, page numbers.

    Studer, Trina. "Sights of Switzerland." <u>*Travel Europe*</u>*, April 2022, pp. 16–18.*

Basic format for an internet article

Last name, First name of author. "Title of Article." <u>Name of</u>
    <u>Website</u>, URL.

    Sutter, Selina. "A Trip through Switzerland." <u>*Swiss Travels,*</u>
    www.swisstravels.com/atripthroughswitzerland.

Diagramming Models

A **diagram** of a sentence shows how the words in the sentence relate to each other. To diagram a sentence, begin with the most important words: the simple subject and simple predicate.

> The simple subject is the main noun or pronoun in the complete subject. The simple predicate is the main verb in the complete predicate.

> A vertical line crosses the base line and separates the subject part from the predicate part of the sentence.

The little frog jumped into the pond.

simple subject	simple predicate

A **compound subject** has two or more simple subjects that share the same predicate. Conjunctions *and* or *or* connect the subjects.

Frogs and crickets jump.

Diagramming Models

A **compound predicate** has two or more simple predicates that share the same subject. Conjunctions *and* or *or* connect the verbs.

Frogs jump *and* swim *in the pond.*

A **compound sentence** contains two simple sentences connected by a comma and a conjunction. Conjunctions *and*, *or*, or *but* can join two simple sentences.

Frogs jump on land, and they swim under water.

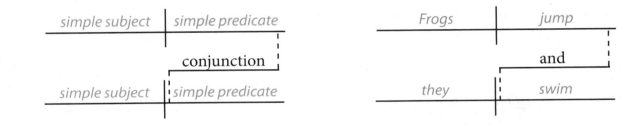

Continued

Diagramming Models

Sentences can have different types of verbs. The type of verb will determine how the sentence is diagrammed. An **action verb** tells what the subject does. A **helping verb** helps the main verb. The complete verb includes the helping verb and the main verb.

The frog is croaking loudly.

simple subject	helping verb main verb		frog	is croaking

A **linking verb** tells what the subject is by connecting the subject to a noun, pronoun, or adjective in the predicate. Notice how the slanted line points from the predicate noun or predicate adjective back toward the subject.

|A predicate noun renames the subject.

Frogs are amphibians.

simple subject	linking verb \ predicate noun		Frogs	are \ amphibians

|A predicate adjective describes the subject.

Frogs are slimy.

simple subject	linking verb \ predicate adjective		Frogs	are \ slimy

Diagramming Models

A **direct object** is a noun in the predicate of the sentence. On a diagram, the line between the action verb and the direct object comes to the base of the line but does not cross it. The line between the action verb and the direct object is straight.

The frog caught a fly.

simple subject	action verb	direct object
frog	caught	fly

An **adjective** is a word that describes a noun. Adjectives answer the question *what kind?* or *how many?* The words *a*, *an*, and **the** are special adjectives called **articles**. On a diagram the adjective is on a slanted line under the noun it describes.

The large frog sat beside a pond.

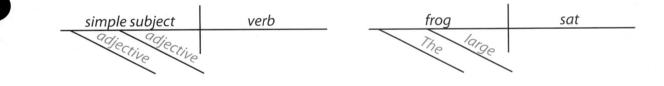

Adverbs describe verbs. They tell *how*, *when*, or *where* something happens. On a diagram, the adverb is on a slanted line under the verb it describes.

The large frog sat quietly beside a pond.

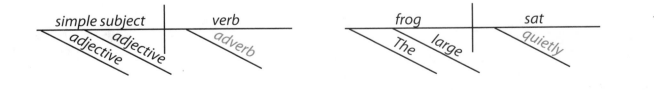

Photo Credits

Chapter 1

2t Daniel Parent/500px/500Px Plus/Getty Images; 2c Ron and Patty Thomas/E+/Getty Images; 2b Jenny Dettrick/Moment/Getty Images; 6 IRYNA KURILOVYCH/iStock/Getty Images Plus/Getty Images; 8 kruwt/iStock/Getty Images Plus/Getty Images; 12 mtreasure/iStock/Getty Images Plus/Getty Images; 14 Andrey Donnikov/iStock/Getty Images Plus/Getty Images; 20 arka38/Shutterstock.com

Chapter 2

31 squiremi/iStock/Getty Images Plus/Getty Images; 32l TennesseePhotographer/iStock/Getty Images Plus/Getty Images; 32c Jay_Zynism/iStock/Getty Images Plus/Getty Images; 32r manonallard/E+/Getty Images; 34 ithinksky/E+/Getty Images

Chapter 3

46 Vadim Sadovski/Shutterstock.com; 48 Donaldson Collection/Michael Ochs Archives/Getty Images; 50 Deejpilot/E+/Getty Images; 54 Gordon Bell/Shutterstock.com; 56 Wojtek Laski/Hulton Archive/Getty Images; 58 huafires/iStock/Getty Images Plus/Getty Images; 59 Robert Sarnowski/Shutterstock.com; 68 neil bowman/iStock/Getty Images Plus/Getty Images; 69 dzika_mrowka/iStock/Getty Images Plus/Getty Images

Chapter 5

101 franckreporter/E+/Getty Images; 102 wizardofwonders/iStock/Getty Images Plus/Getty Images; 113 fotoMonkee/iStock/Getty Images Plus/Getty Images; 120 ozflash/iStock/Getty Images Plus/Getty Images; 124 Tamara Harding/iStock/Getty Images Plus/Getty Images

Chapter 6

130 razihusin/iStock/Getty Images Plus/Getty Images; 137 GlobalP/iStock/Getty Images Plus/Getty Images; 138 SDI Productions/E+/Getty Images

Chapter 7

158 Frankhuang/iStock/Getty Images Plus/Getty Images; 159 Nataliia_Melnychuk/iStock/Getty Images Plus/Getty Images

Chapter 8

182 "Robert Moffat" by George Baxter/Wikimedia Commons/Public Domain; 183 Photon-Photos/iStock/Getty Images Plus/Getty Images; 184 1001slide/E+/Getty Images; 192 Leonid Andronov/iStock/Getty Images Plus/Getty Images; 194 Melih Evren Burus/iStock/Getty Images Plus/Getty Images; 196 Pictorial Press Ltd/Alamy Stock Photo; 202 Veronika7833/iStock/Getty Images Plus/Getty Images; 205 "Mary Slessor"/Wikimedia Commons/Public Domain; 206 SKLA/iStock/Getty Images Plus/Getty Images

Chapter 9

216t makasana/iStock/Getty Images Plus/Getty Images; 216b Jeff McGraw/Shutterstock.com; 221 Nahhan/iStock/Getty Images Plus/Getty Images; 222 George Ostertag/Alamy Stock Photo; 224 imageBROKER/Alamy Stock Photo; 227 Geoorgiy Boyko/Shutterstock.com; 233 Gary Kavanagh/iStock/Getty Images Plus/Getty Images; 234l flocu/iStock/Getty Images Plus/Getty Images; 234r alan64/iStock/Getty Images Plus/Getty Images; 237 Mariakray/iStock/Getty Images Plus/Getty Images

Chapter 11

271 kickstand/E+/Getty Images; 275 LIKE HE/iStock/Getty Images Plus/Getty Images; 276 ehrlif/iStock/Getty Images Plus/Getty Images; 278 ChrisBoswell/iStock/Getty Images Plus/Getty Images; 279 Ed Jackson/iStock/Getty Images Plus/Getty Images; 281 Allan Wood Photography/Shutterstock.com

Chapter 12

292t 2p2play/Shutterstock.com; 292c Sean Pavone/iStock/Getty Images Plus/Getty Images; 292b chengyuzheng/iStock/Getty Images Plus/Getty Images; 294l Images By Kenny/Shutterstock.com; 294c hxdyl/iStock/Getty Images Plus/Getty Images; 294r kali9/E+/Getty Images; 295l, 299l tiler84/iStock/Getty Images Plus/Getty Images; 295r, 299r Epitavi/Shutterstock.com; 303 dszc/E+/Getty Images; 307t T.M.O.Pictures/Alamy Stock Photo; 307b Viktor Makhnov/iStock/Getty Images Plus/Getty Images

Chapter 13

314 (jaguar) Klein and Hubert/Minden Pictures; 314 (church) Global_Pics/iStock Unreleased/Getty Images; 314 (torch) Anastasiia Lagoda/Shutterstock.com; 314 (statue) luoman/iStock Unreleased/Getty Images; 325 Adobe Stock/Тарас Нагирняк; 327 FG Trade/iStock/Getty Images Plus/Getty Images; 328 Eric Nathan/Alamy Stock Photo; 329 Michel VIARD/iStock/Getty Images Plus/Getty Images; 331t LeoMercon/iStock/Getty Images Plus/Getty Images; 331b phive2015/iStock/Getty Images Plus/Getty Images; 332 vadimguzhva/iStock/Getty Images Plus/Getty Images

Chapter 14

340 (Swiss flag) mehmetbuma/iStock/Getty Images Plus/Getty Images; 340 (palm tree) piovesempre/iStock/Getty Images Plus/Getty Images; 340 (alpenhorn) saiko3p/iStock Editorial/Getty Images Plus/Getty Images; 340 (St. Bernard) swisshippo/iStock/Getty Images Plus/Getty Images; 340 (ice sculpture) PUMPZA/Shutterstock.com; 340 (chocolate bar) gcpics/Shutterstock.com; 340 (cheese) PicturePartners/iStock/Getty Images Plus/Getty Images; 340 (pine marten) Ludmila Ruzickova/Shutterstock.com; 340 (Dufourspitze) Nicola Colombo/iStock/Getty Images/Getty Images; 340 (Alpine ibex) renelo/iStock/Getty Images Plus/Getty Images; 344 Andrew Mayovskyy/Shutterstock.com; 345 Xantana/iStock/Getty Images Plus/Getty Images; 349 Anna Nahabed/Shutterstock.com; 353 AerialVision_it/Shutterstock.com

Acknowledgments

Chapter 2

Lerner Publishing: "Piano" and front cover image from BOW-TIE PASTA by Brian P. Cleary, illustrated by Andy Rowland. Text copyright © 2016 by Brian P. Cleary. Illustration copyright © 2016 by Lerner Publishing Group, Inc. Reprinted with the permission of Millbrook Press, a division of Lerner Publishing Group, Inc. All rights reserved. No part of this excerpt may be used or reproduced in any manner whatsoever without the prior written permission of Lerner Publishing Group, Inc.

Houghton Mifflin Harcourt: "Top Secret" and front cover image from BOOKSPEAK!: Poems About Books by Laura Purdie Salas. Text copyright © 2011 by Laura Purdie Salas. Jacket illustrations © 2011 by Josee Bisaillon. Reprinted by permission of Houghton Mifflin Harcourt Publishing Company. All rights reserved.

Chapter 3

NASA: Excerpt from article by Dan Stillman, "What is the Hubble Space Telescope?" National Aeronautics and Space Administration. April 24, 2020. nasa.gov.

Chapter 4

JourneyForth: Excerpt from *Silent Road to Rescue* by Denise Williamson. Copyright © 2008 BJU Press. All rights reserved.

Chapter 5

Roaring Brook Press: Text excerpt, front cover image, and illustration from REDWOODS © 2009 by Jason Chin. Reprinted by permission of Roaring Brook Press, a division of Holtzbrinck Publishing Holdings Limited Partnership. All rights reserved.

Chapter 6

Lerner Publishing: Text excerpt and front cover image from HOOP GENIUS by John Coy, illustrated by Joe Morse. Text copyright © 2013 by John Coy. Illustration copyright © 2013 by Joe Morse. Reprinted with the permission of Carolrhoda Books, a division of Lerner Publishing Group, Inc. All rights reserved. No part of this excerpt may be used or reproduced in any manner whatsoever without the prior written permission of Lerner Publishing Group, Inc.

Chapter 7

Houghton Mifflin Harcourt: Text excerpt and front cover image from A DAY'S WORK by Eve Bunting, illustrated by Ron Himler. Text copyright © 1994 by Eve Bunting. Cover illustrations © 1994 by Ronald Himler. Reprinted by permission of Clarion Books, an imprint of Houghton Mifflin Company. All rights reserved.

Chapter 8

Gospel Fellowship Association: Adapted from an article by Dr. John A. Dreisbach, "Robert Moffat." Gospel Fellowship Association. June 14, 1999. https://gfamissions.org. Used by permission.

Chapter 9

Cherry Lake Publishing: Text excerpt and front cover image from D IS FOR DESERT by Barbara Gowan, Copyright © 2012. Illustration Copyright © 2012 by Gijsbert van Frankenhuyzen. Used by permission of Cherry Lake Publishing.

Chapter 11

Charlesbridge Publishing: Text excerpt, front cover image and illustration for "Angel Island Light Station" from *Safely to Shore: America's Lighthouses* by Iris Van Rynbach. Copyright © 2003 by Iris Van Rynbach. Used with permission by Charlesbridge Publishing, Inc. www.charlesbridge.com. All rights reserved.

Chapter 12

JourneyForth: Excerpt from *Peanut Butter Friends* by Deb Brammer. Copyright © 1994 BJU Press. All rights reserved.